SOVIET ARMOUR
SINCE 1945
BRYAN PERRETT

SINCE 1945

BRYAN PERRETT

BLANDFORD PRESS
LONDON · NEW YORK · SYDNEY

First published in the UK in 1987 by Blandford Press
Artillery House, Artillery Row, London SW1P 1RT

Copyright © Bryan Perett 1987

Distributed in the United States by
Sterling Publishing Co, Inc,
2 Park Avenue, New York, NY 10016

Distributed in Australia by
Capricorn Link (Australia) Pty Ltd
PO Box 665, Lane Cove, NSW 2066

British Library Cataloguing in Publication Data

Perett, Bryan
    Soviet armour since 1945.—(Hardware)
    1. Soviet Union—Armed forces—
    Equipment—History   I. Title II. Series
    623′0947   UC208

ISBN 0 7137 1735 1

Series editor: M. G. Burns

Typeset by Keyspools Ltd, Golborne, Lancs
Printed in Great Britain by
R. J. Acford, Chichester

CONTENTS

In the years following the Civil War of 1917–22 the Soviet Union found itself to be something of an international outcast. The same was true of the Weimar Republic of Germany and it was natural that the two should collaborate by setting up secret fighting vehicle experimental stations deep within Russia at Kazan and Voronezh. Despite this, and intense study of the best features of contemporary foreign designs, in 1928 the Soviet Army could field no more than 92 tanks, all of them obsolete. Then came a series of Five Year Plans which rationalised tank manufacture to such an extent that by 1935 there were over 10,000 tanks in service with subsequent annual totals continuing to rise steadily. During this period certain trends became apparent which were to remain constant features of Russian tank design, including the adoption of the V-12 aluminium alloy diesel engine, the provision of wide tracks for driving in the worst conditions that deep snow and the mud of the spring thaw could produce, and the mounting of larger calibre guns than could generally be found on the tanks of other armies.

A wide variety of tank types was produced, including the multi-turreted T-100 and T-35 heavy tanks intended for the breakthrough role, the T-26 and the somewhat larger T-28 for direct infantry support, the fast BT series for deep penetration operations, and the light amphibious T-37, T-38 and T-40 for reconnaissance. The technical lessons learned during this phase were incorporated in the superlative T-34 medium tank and the heavily armoured KV (Klimenti Voroshilov) series, both of which entered service in 1940.

However, while startling progress had been made in the technical sphere, the armoured corps' doctrine was repeatedly hamstrung by political considerations and the failure of inexperienced commanders to interpret events correctly. The Soviet Army, like the German, did not think simply in terms of strategy, i.e. the planning of a campaign, the tactics, and execution at the local level by troops on the ground, but interposed a third level known as operative or more commonly nowadays, operational; this specialised in the conduct of operations at corps level, but could extend as high as army. Equally, while the writings of Major-General J. F. C. Fuller and Captain B. H. Liddell Hart emphasised the full potential conferred by the adoption of mechanised warfare, in Germany and in Russia their ideas simply dovetailed with older thought processes. Thus, with very few exceptions, the Panzer leaders of the Third Reich were all products of the Imperial war machine and as junior officers had thoroughly absorbed the principles of *Vernichtungsgedanke* or Annihilation Concept propounded by Clausewitz. The *Blitzkrieg* technique, therefore, was built on foundations that were long established. Similarly, there were former Czarist officers who recognised the connection during the Soviet armoured corps' formative years, notably V. K. Triandafillov, an artilleryman, who in 1927 published a book entitled *The Character of the Operations of Modern Armies* in which he quoted Fuller's ideas and emphasised the need for surprise at every level, the generation of intense violence on a limited frontage to obtain a quick, clean breakthrough to operational depth, followed immediately by a high tempo advance to the strategic objective; simultaneously he stressed that mechanised formations must not allow themselves to become bogged down in the battles of their non-mechanised colleagues.

Triandafillov died while still young but his theories were adopted with enthusiasm by another former Czarist officer of great standing and reputation, M. N. Tukhachevsky, shortly to become a Marshal of the Soviet Union. In his book *Red Armour* Richard Simpkin puts forward the tenable suggestion that if Triandafillov was Russia's Clausewitz, then Tukhachevsky can be regarded as her Guderian. From 1930 onwards Tukhachevsky concentrated on the formation of mechanised corps with which the theories of deep operational penetration could have been implemented. These formations have been criticised on the

Even before the outbreak of the Great Patriotic War the Soviet Army possessed the world's largest tank fleet, but the majority of its more radical thinkers on mechanised warfare perished during the Great Purge. The photograph shows a simulated attack by T-26 tanks, supported by a squadron of Polikarpov Po-2 ground-attack aircraft, during the 1935 Kiev Exercises. The T-26 first saw combat in the Spanish Civil War, and the Po-2 remained active throughout World War 2 *(Novosti)*.

ground that the ratio of tanks to mechanised infantry was too high, but the majority of contemporary armies were guilty of the same mistake. Rather more telling was the lack of an adequate command, control and communications apparatus (C^3 in modern parlance) since this meant that once formations were actually committed to action in accordance with a mandatory pre-designated plan, their commanders were unable to exercise their function in what might be radically altered circumstances. This resulted partly from the lack of sufficient tank radio sets, partly from the low level of secondary technical education which was unable to produce enough men able to operate and maintain them anyway, and partly because of a rigid structure of command imposed by a political system which discouraged personal initiative.

Given time, it is probable that Tukhachevsky could have eliminated the majority of these snags, but it was not to be. Stalin saw him as a dangerous rival and the armoured corps as a nest of nascent Praetorianism. In June 1937 Tukhachevsky and his principal supporters were arrested, then court-marshalled and shot. In the months that followed the Soviet officer corps was ruthlessly purged from top to bottom, thousands being executed on the flimsiest evidence while thousands more simply disappeared or were sent to labour camps. Those who survived this reign of terror were too cowed to do more than passively await orders and then obey them to the letter.

The mechanised corps were disbanded and their armoured elements re-assigned to direct infantry support, largely on the recommendation of General D. G. Pavlov, the commander of the Russian tank force which had been sent to assist the Republican government in the Spanish Civil War. Pavlov's tanks had actually broken through into the enemy's hinterland on several occasions but had always been forced to

retire; what he failed to see was that if the tanks had been accompanied by mechanised infantry the captured ground could have been consolidated and a favourable situation further exploited. In his view, however, the deep operational theory had been discredited and Stalin was only too pleased to take his advice. In passing, it is worth mentioning that the T-26s and BTs sent to Spain proved so superior to the Nationalists' little PzKpfw Is and Italian tankettes that von Thoma, commanding the German Condor Legion's tank troops, offered cash rewards for any that could be captured intact.

In September 1939 the Soviet Army entered Poland while hostilities were still in progress between that country and Germany. The clumsy handling of the demoralised Soviet armour gave the Germans a false impression of Russian potential and was a factor taken into account when planning the invasion of Russia itself less than two years later. Nor did the Winter War of 1939–40 against Finland win the armoured corps any laurels, for during the rigidly conducted Russian set-piece attacks against Finnish positions on the Karelian isthmus the Finns were able to pin down the Soviet infantry, so separating it from its supporting armour, and although the latter was on occasion able to penetrate the Finnish rear areas its isolated tanks were, more often than not, stalked and destroyed by tank-hunting parties.

Nonetheless, there was some cause for optimism, for in the Far East aggressive Japanese incursions across the Manchurian frontier were sharply chastised in August 1939 during a notable action on the River Khalkhin. Being far removed from the seat of power, Soviet troops in the Far East tended to enjoy rather more autonomy than was the case elsewhere and in this instance were commanded by General Georgi Zhukov, an officer whose loyalty to Stalin was not in question. Zhukov chose to fight a battle in the Tukhachevsky mould, using an independent armoured brigade to smash its way through the Japanese flank and establish a block behind the enemy lines, which were then attacked by the main Soviet force. Out-thought and out-fought, the Japanese were so thoroughly routed that even when the fortunes of the Soviet Union were at their lowest ebb during the Great Patriotic War they did not attempt to renew the contest.

Faced with such self-evident truths as the victory at Khalkin-Gol and the superb handling of the German *Panzer* corps in Poland and in the West the following year, Stalin and his supporters had little option but to reverse their earlier decision and re-establish the recently disbanded mechanised corps. This was done hastily and often produced an incompatible mixture of vehicles, many of them in poor mechanical shape; worse, very few officers had experience of handling such formations and the majority were still disinclined to use their personal initiative in the wake of terror left by the Great Purge; worse still, even the units which formed the constituent tank divisions of the mechanised corps were unused to working together and little training had been done when, on 22 June 1941, the Wehrmacht launched its invasion under the codename of Operation BARBAROSSA.

At this period the Soviet Army possessed approximately 24,000 tanks, outnumbering the *Panzerwaffe* by 7:1, although at the point of contact the ratio was obviously much smaller. It was, however, immediately apparent that the German armour was opposed by a flawed enemy and while many Russian tank units fought with suicidal bravery they were unable to cope with the expertise of the battle-hardened *Panzertruppen*. In the south, by dint of superhuman effort, Colonel-General Mikhail Kirponos managed to concentrate no less than six of the ungainly mechanised corps against the armoured spearheads of Field Marshal von Rundstedt's Army Group South and a furious *mêlée* raged around Brody for four days, the largest tank battle of the war thus far. In the end, the inexperience of the Russians and the intervention of the *Luftwaffe* led to Kirponos' withdrawal and ultimate encirclement in the notorious Kiev Pocket.

Ultimately, Hitler's meddling in the conduct of the campaign was to cost him the decisive victory he sought, the onset of the worst winter in living memory and a counter-offensive by tough Siberian divisions combining to stabilise the front. By then the Soviet armoured corps had lost about 20,000 tanks, including the majority of the older types, and Pavlov, still regarded as the Army's expert on tank warfare, had been shot by Stalin for his failure to halt the enemy's advance earlier. On the other hand, the vital tank manufacturing plants had been dismantled lock, stock and barrel and transported eastwards beyond the range of the *Luftwaffe*'s bombers, where they soon began producing armoured fighting vehicles (AFVs) in numbers that Germany could not hope to equal.

The subsequent history of the Great Patriotic War is too well known to require more than the briefest summary here. The 1942 campaign began with a local counter-offensive intended to recapture Kharkov; this failed badly and demonstrated that the Russians still had much to learn. The German advance into the Caucasus followed almost immediately, accompanied by an attempt to capture Stalingrad which soon assumed precedence in Hitler's mind. In November the Soviet Army launched its first major application of *Blitzkrieg*, Operation URANUS, a brilliant double-envelopment orchestrated by Zhukov, trapping the German Sixth Army in Stalingrad and compelling its surrender the following February, although an attempted follow-through intended to isolate the German armies withdrawing from the Caucasus was expertly foiled by von Manstein's Army Group South. The legacy of these operations was a huge salient in the line around Kursk against which Hitler concentrated most of his armour, hoping to eliminate it with converging thrusts through the northern and southern shoulders and thereby inflict such punitive casualties that Stalin would settle for a negotiated peace. The Russians were well aware of his intentions and laid out a defence in depth with substantial armoured reserves lying close behind the front. Operation CITADEL, as the German offensive was known, began on 5 July 1943 and was cancelled a week later having made scant progress, although it witnessed the largest tank battle in history. The Soviet Army promptly went over to the attack and retained the strategic initiative for the remainder of the war.

With every month that passed the handling of its armoured formations became more confident. At the tactical level it continued to sustain losses that any other army might have regarded as crippling, but it continued to attain its objectives at the operational level, assisted by Hitler's obstinate refusal to sanction voluntary local withdrawals that would have benefited the Wehrmacht's overall situation. On 22 June 1944, the third anniversary of the German invasion, the USSR initiated Operation BAGRATION, resulting in the destruction of the enemy's Army Group Centre. This was one of the Soviet armoured corps' most outstanding achievements of the war, no less than 40 tank brigades breaking through on a 250-mile front and advancing 450 miles in four weeks, isolating objectives and creating pockets of trapped enemy formations just as the *Panzerwaffe* had three years earlier. Thereafter, operations were maintained at a slower but equally remorseless pace until Berlin itself was stormed in May 1945. In August the armoured corps crowned its achievements during the Great Patriotic War by virtually destroying the Japanese Kwantung Army in Manchuria in a remarkable operation which involved the rapid and efficient initial deployment of over 5,000 AFVs.

The last two years of the war are regarded by the Russians as containing the bedrock experience upon which their present-day theories of armoured warfare have been constructed and naturally they continue to be studied in great depth. As the methods evolved continued to be used long after the war they are discussed more fully elsewhere, although it is worth mentioning that at the time the failure to develop an armoured personnel carrier (APC) contributed materially to the high casualties incurred, as did the absence of self-propelled artillery—other than assault guns and tank destroyers—to a lesser extent.

Conversely, two continuous threads dominated the Soviet approach to mechanised war in the years between 1941 and 1945. The first and most obvious was the need to keep ahead in the technical race as each side progressively introduced more powerful tank guns and thicker defensive armour. The second was an unqualified acceptance of Tukhachevsky's concept of the deep battle and the urgent need to train senior commanders in the handling of armoured formations, *force majeure*, in action. This began in a modest way with small tank brigades in December 1941, progressed to tank corps, each of three tank brigades, one motor rifle brigade and supporting arms, by mid-1942, and only months later had reached the level of the tank army, consisting of two tank

Overleaf: **A set-piece attack in the Ukraine during the winter of 1943/44. The Soviets paid a heavy price for their failure to develop armoured personnel carriers (APCs) as their infantry were more often than not pinned down by artillery fire, leaving the tanks vulnerable to the enemy's anti-tank gun screens. Such attacks as this were frequently repeated at terrible cost until the defence was worn down. The tanks are T-34/76s** *(Novosti)*.

and one mechanised corps plus supporting arms.

Thus, in May 1945 the Western Allies found themselves confronted by a tank force which both outnumbered and outgunned them, was impressively armoured, possessed apparently limitless resources having received 29,000 AFVs from the tank manufacturing plants the previous year alone, and whose senior commanders had earned the sincere respect of their former German foes. It was true that its procedures lacked the flexibility of their own, but obviously they worked and had ensured a continuous run of victories for the past two years. In the light of Stalin's unfriendly, not to say belligerent attitudes, such discoveries provoked intense concern.

Today the Soviet Union possesses the largest fleet of AFVs the world has ever seen and has, in fact, done so for the past two generations. That this fleet continues to expand not only in size but also in the diversity of its equipment, coupled with the fact that it is clearly organised for offensive operations, has done nothing to allay the alarm of the West, which is only too aware of the Marxist-Leninist dogma that communist-style revolution must spread throughout the world, by force of arms if necessary.

The perspective from within the Kremlin is, however, somewhat altered. There, the present-day rulers of the USSR take a less intense view of world revolution than did the founding fathers of the Soviet system. It is certainly still regarded as being a desirable objective to be pursued whenever possible by non-violent or surrogate means, although no time-scale is laid down and the direct involvement of the armed forces of the Soviet Union is looked upon as a last resort to be used only in circumstances which actually threaten the existence of the USSR or its cordon of satellite states. Such circumstances were considered to exist in the German Democratic Republic in 1953, in Hungary in 1956 and in Czechoslovakia in 1968, all being regarded as police actions necessary for the preservation of the Warsaw Pact's integrity. The invasion of Afghanistan in December 1979 was an uncharacteristic departure from this principle and a serious miscalculation resulting in a situation from which extrication is presently proving almost impossible. Nonetheless, even excluding nuclear factors, an outright war on the scale of World War 2 is a prospect which every Soviet citizen regards with horror and we have only to consider in the briefest terms Russia's cruel historical experience this century to understand why such a huge standing army is looked upon as a necessity by the man in the street.

During World War 1 it is estimated that Russia sustained ten million casualties, including 2,500,000 dead and 1,450,000 permanently disabled. Several million more perished in the Civil War and in Stalin's merciless purges. But during World War 2, or the Great Patriotic War as it is known in the USSR, Russian casualties in dead alone amounted to a staggering *twenty million*, military and civilian, while an area equivalent to the whole of England and Wales south of a line drawn between the Mersey and the Humber was utterly laid waste after being fought over time and again. Small wonder, then, that this experience has burned itself into the Russian consciousness in a manner unimaginable in the West. The overriding consideration since has been that any future war must be fought on the enemy's soil and not on Russia's—hence the need for an army trained almost exclusively in the techniques of offensive warfare and the added security of a cordon of Soviet-dominated states which, with the USSR, form the Warsaw Pact.

Whatever the truth, the Russians believe that the West left them to carry the burden of two terrible world wars almost unaided, and they are unlikely to change their minds. They still distrust the West and do not see NATO as being essentially a defensive alliance, but rather as an alliance with a potential for aggression, thereby reflecting the Western view of the Warsaw Pact. The frequent comment that the latter is equipped well beyond the scale appropriate to defence is answered by its declared intention of carrying the war to the enemy. This demands, of course, that the odds must be in the attacker's favour and the Russians have, therefore, had to decide on what *they* believe to be the appropriate ratio, taking into account the fearful losses inflicted by the outnumbered *Wehrmacht* during the last years of the Great Patriotic War and NATO's undoubted ability to do likewise; it is far from improbable that many senior Russian officers consider even the present extremely favourable odds as being quite inadequate.

Be this as it may, the Soviet Army at the present time is believed to possess about 56,000 tanks plus an equivalent number of

During 1944 the Soviet Army became more experienced in the techniques of exploiting a breakthrough and its deep penetrations often resulted in the encirclement of German formations which were trapped by Hitler's rigid orders to hold their ground. These T-34/76s each carry an infantry section armed with sub-machine-guns. Cavalry also played a significant role in Soviet high-mobility operations on the more open sectors of the Eastern Front *(Novosti)*.

armoured personnel carriers, supported by self-propelled artillery and an impressive array of assault engineer equipment. Superficially this immense concentration of force, consisting of 52 tank divisions, 117 motor rifle divisions and eight airborne divisions, appears capable of rolling over anything in its path, although it should also be remembered that only a portion of it is directly deployed against NATO; the demands of the longest land frontier in the world, the need to maintain a large armed presence in the Far East, where a troubled relationship with the People's Republic of China has occasionally degenerated into armed conflict, and the necessary provision of a central reserve have all induced a wide degree of dispersion. Again, not even the economy of the USSR, geared as it is to the manufacture of arms rather than consumer goods, can afford to keep such a huge army on a war footing. Only 22 tank, 32 motor rifle and the eight airborne divisions are presently listed as being Category I, i.e. at over 75 per cent of their strength in personnel and equipment and

ready to take the field; 30 tank and 25 motor rifle divisions are defined as Category II, i.e. at between 50 and 75 per cent of their strength but theoretically capable of deployment within thirty days of mobilisation; a further 60 motor rifle divisions are classed as Category III and are maintained on a cadre basis at between 10 and 33 per cent of their strength, deployment being unlikely in less than 60 days unless several of these formations pool their resources, although the armies of the Warsaw Pact allies balance the initial shortfall to a limited extent. This may well bring the overall situation into sharper focus but it cannot diminish the fact that the Soviet Army has been forged and reforged continuously into a formidable weapon capable of applying its own evolutionary doctrine of mechanised warfare with an efficiency unequalled in its history, employing thousands of fighting vehicles designed specifically to meet the requirements of the offensive battle it believes one day it may have to fight.

The T-34/85 required a redesigned three-man turret to house the larger main armament. This example, photographed in the Balkans during the final days of the war, has obviously been subjected to hard usage. The drum at the rear is a jettison fuel tank fitted to increase the tank's operational range. Wide tracks and a Christie suspension enabled the T-34 to cope with going so bad that German tanks were rendered immobile, earning the vehicle the nickname of the 'Snow King' *(IWM)*.

For almost a decade after the end of the Great Patriotic War the Soviet Army remained equipped with the same generation of tanks which had won it the tremendous victories of 1944 and 1945, including the T-34 medium and the IS (Iosef Stalin) heavy series, both of which gave Western designers considerable food for thought.

In the USSR it has long been the custom to establish design bureaux which concentrate their specialist skills on a particular area of defence requirements such as tanks, artillery weapons, fixed-wing aircraft of various types and rotocraft. These frequently take their name from the head of the bureau, especially in aviation circles, but in the field of AFV construction the names of two engineers stand out, those of Mikhail Koshkin and Iosef Kotin.

Koshkin headed the team which produced

the T-34, and since this is now regarded as the grandfather of all modern tank design it is worth recapitulating briefly the vehicle's early history. Initially, the Koshkin team had been briefed to provide a replacement for the BT series, which experience in Spain had shown to be too lightly armoured, while retaining its impressive speed and the fine cross-country performance conferred by the Christie suspension. After several contending prototypes were evaluated the T-34 design was standardised in 1940 and entered mass production.

The most remarkable thing about Koshkin's design was that it represented a finely balanced equation between the three basic requirements of tank design, firepower, protection and mobility. The T-34 was armed with a 76.2 mm gun at a time when the tanks of most armies employed 37 mm armour-defeating weapons,

secondary armament consisting of two 7.62 mm machine-guns, one mounted co-axially and the other in the bow. The hull overhung the tracks and was constructed from angled armour plate, the glacis being only 45 mm (1.77 in) thick but laid back at 60 degrees, thereby providing ballistic protection equivalent to a 90 mm (3.5 in) plate in the vertical plane. The tank was powered by a V-2 12-cylinder 500 hp diesel engine and was capable of 50 km/h (31 mph) on the road. Wide tracks enabled it to cope with mud and snow alike, earning the vehicle the nickname of 'The Snow King' among its German opponents, whose own operations were often brought to a standstill by these conditions. Typical of the robust simplicity which went into its design was the method of retaining the track pins, which were inserted unsecured from the inside; a wiper plate was welded to each side of the hull and any pin which had worked loose was knocked back into place as it passed. The crew consisted of commander, who also acted as gunner in the cramped two-man turret, loader, driver and hull gunner.

As the war progressed, the T-34 was progressively upgunned and uparmoured. The main armament of the first series to enter service had a calibre length of L/30.5, but this was quickly replaced by a more powerful weapon of L/41.2 calibres. The last of the 76.2 mm gun versions of the T-34 to be produced was the Model 43, which had 110 mm (4.3 in) frontal armour and was distinguished from earlier types by the addition of an elementary commander's cupola, and this remained in production until the spring of 1945.

In the meantime, the German response to the T-34 had been to re-arm their PzKpfw IVs, assault guns and tank destroyers with 75 mm high velocity guns, accelerate the development of the Tiger and design the Panther from scratch. By 1943 the T-34 had lost its qualitative edge and it was clear that the 76.2 mm gun was rapidly becoming obsolete. It was equally clear that the turret lacked the potential for further up-gunning and it says much for the capacity of Koshkin's basic design that the answer was to fit a new and much larger turret mounting an 85 mm gun. The new turret also contained sufficient room for a gunner, thereby ending the unsatisfactory situation that had existed previously.

The new tank was designated T-34/85 to distinguish it from the earlier models, which were subsequently referred to as T-34/76. It entered service early in 1944, achieving approximate parity with the Panther. It has remained in service ever since with various armies round the world and can thus claim the longest active career of any AFV in history, although by the middle 1950s it was being phased out by the Soviet Army. Since the Great Patriotic War it has seen action in Korea, Egypt, Syria, Vietnam, Cyprus, Angola and Somalia.

In the meantime, thought had also been given to the T-34's eventual successor. One problem with the Christie suspension was that it absorbed much priceless space, the large coil springs being housed vertically within the hull walls. It was decided, therefore, to develop a medium tank employing a torsion bar suspension which, as the bars and their return springs were mounted transversely under the floor, would confer more internal space, the cost being a slightly less comfortable ride.

The new tank, designated T-44, made its appearance in 1945. It bore a marked resemblance to the T-34/85, but was slightly longer despite the engine and final drive being mounted transversely, and a little wider, although at 250 cm (8 ft 2 in) it was also a useful 23 cm (9 in) lower. The track and large Christie-type roadwheels had been retained, but with a wider gap between the first and second pairs; the hull configuration, however, displayed fewer angles and was less complex. The same 85 mm L/51.5 gun was employed, but secondary armament was limited to one machine-gun, mounted co-axially. A lower, more streamlined turret incorporating a low commander's cupola was marred by a prominent rear overhang which presented a serious shot trap. Armour thickness was 80 mm (3.14 in) on the glacis and 110 mm (4.3 in) on the mantlet. The engine had been up-rated to produce 520 hp at 2,000 rpm so that in spite of being slightly heavier than the T-34/85, the T-44 was actually a little faster. In the absence of a hull machine-gun, the crew was reduced to four, viz. commander, gunner, loader and driver.

Some 200 T-44s were built and although they did replace the T-34/85 in some medium tank regiments, the design was regarded as being intermediate and not sufficiently radical to warrant a major production run on its own merits. Indeed, the question of further up-gunning the medium tank fleet required im-

mediate consideration as the US Army already had a 90 mm tank gun in service and by 1947 the British Army's 20-pdr (83.4 mm) Centurion Mark III had entered production. Nonetheless, the T-44 represented a most important step along the road towards the Soviet Army's first post-war medium tank design, the T-54, which is discussed in the next chapter. At least one T-44 unit is known to have participated in the Budapest street battles of 1956 but by the end of the 1950s the vehicle had been withdrawn from first-line service.

The second strand of development which continued after the Great Patriotic War, albeit briefly, was that of heavy tank design. This was a field which had been dominated by the Iosef Kotin design team and in 1941 the *Wehrmacht* had probably been more shaken by its encounter with Kotin's KVs than it had been by those with Koshkin's T-34/76s. The KV-1 was armed with the same 76.2 mm gun as in the T-34 and the less numerous KV-2 with a 152 mm howitzer, but what had impressed the Germans most was the apparent invulnerability conferred by the massive 110 mm (4.3 in) frontal armour plating, although this was

less scientifically arranged than in Koshkin's design.

Following the appearance of better German tanks in the shape of the later marks of the PzKpfw IV, the Tiger and the Panther, criticism of the KV began to grow within the Soviet armoured corps, specifically that it lacked the agility yet was no better armed than the T-34/76; in other words, like the British Churchill, which also saw service with Russian heavy tank regiments, it represented a case of being too much tank for too little gun. By 1943 the KV had clearly had its day, although Kotin was already well advanced with the design of its successor, the IS, for which an 85 mm main armament had been selected. In September of that year, however, manufacture of the IS was still some months away and the decision was taken to prolong the KV's life as an interim measure by marrying the IS turret and 85 mm gun to the KV hull, the combination being known as the KV-85.

The first of the IS series to be built retained the 85 mm gun, but as the same calibre weapon now armed the upgunned T-34/85 the original criticism remained unanswered. It was de-

cided, therefore, to take a major step forward by adopting a 122 mm L/43 artillery weapon, with double-baffle muzzle brake, as this gave an excellent performance with both armour-piercing and high explosive ammunition. This was fitted as standard on the IS-2 and retrospectively re-armed those IS-1s which had already been completed with the 85 mm gun. The first 122 mm guns to be fitted retained their original interrupted-screw breech pending the introduction of a more convenient falling-block mechanism. A major disadvantage was the sheer bulk of the ammunition, which was split into projectile and propellant for ease of handling in the confined space of the turret, the result being a rate of fire amounting to only three or four rounds per minute. Again, only 28 rounds could be stowed, which was far from satisfactory, although these drawbacks were considered acceptable in view of the gun's ability to penetrate 185 mm (7.3 in) of armour at 1,000 yd.

The running gear of the IS series was similar to that of the KV, each set consisting of six small-steel-tyred road-wheels suspended from torsion bars, three return rollers, front idler and rear drive sprocket. The hull, however, had been re-designed so that it overhung the wide tracks and incorporated heavy castings in its 120 mm (4.7 in) frontal armour. The vehicle weighed 45.72 tonnes (45 UK tons, 41.5 US tons) and was powered by a 12-cylinder 520 hp

V-2 diesel engine which could produce a maximum speed on good going of 37 km/h (23 mph). The crew consisted of commander, gunner, loader and driver.

The IS-2 was first issued to heavy breakthrough tank regiments in early 1944. These operated under the direct control of army commanders, but such was their success that a heavy regiment was later attached to each tank corps whenever possible, and finally heavy tank brigades were formed, each of three IS-2 regiments. The tank was considered to be fully the equal of the Panther, while the Tiger was only able to penetrate it at 1,800 m (1,970 yd), at which range it was itself vulnerable to the 122 mm gun. Some 3,400 IS-2s were built during the Great Patriotic War, the vehicle remaining in service with the Soviet and Warsaw Pact armies until well into the 1950s. The IS-2 was also supplied in small numbers to the armies of the People's Republic of China and to Cuba.

Whatever the essential virtues of Soviet tank design, contemporary Western observers tended to criticise the coarse standard of finish in general and that of the IS-2 in particular. To this the Russians responded that the urgency of the situation and the average life expectancy of AFVs did not warrant such attention. On the other hand, it was conceded that given the basic requirements of the IS-2, i.e. the 122 mm gun, a high protection factor and the need to

The IS-2 heavy tank was coarsely finished but heavily armoured and was armed with a 122 mm gun. It saw extensive service during the last year of the Great Patriotic War, being a match for the Panther but not the Tiger.

The IS-3 heavy tank entered service in 1945, its combination of split glacis plate, domed turret and 122 mm gun causing Western tank designers serious concern for a while. The vehicle's pointed prow earned it the Russian nickname of *Shchuka* (Pike) *(IWM)*.

contain overall weight, the design could only benefit from a more scientific armour layout. The task was given to an engineer named Dukhov and his team, who produced their prototype IS-3 in November 1944. Some 350 had been built by the end of the war and thereafter it replaced the IS-2 on the production lines.

Dukhov's IS-3 layout influenced post-war tank design almost as much as did Koshkin's T-34. The low, domed turret that was for so long to become a hallmark of Russian tanks was here seen for the first time and made a most favourable impression with its clean ballistic lines, although less immediately apparent was the lack of working headroom that would particularly affect the loader and, more importantly, the very limited gun depression available because of the need to curtail the upwards travel of the breech in such a confined space, the consequence of the latter being that the tank was unable to take full advantage of the cover provided by reverse slopes, having to move forward onto the crest to engage targets just below the horizontal. The hull armour was sharply angled, its most striking feature being the glacis, which consisted of two five-sided plates laid back and joined in the form of a flat V, thereby providing deflection surfaces as well as enhancing the inherent thickness of the plates. This configuration produced the sharp prow which earned the vehicle its Russian

nickname of *Shchuka* or 'The Pike'. It is a measure of Dukhov's achievement that although the IS-3's frontal armour was 200 mm (7.87 in) thick the vehicle weighed slightly *less* than the IS-2 and at 203 cm (8 ft) stood 30.5 cm (1 ft) lower, while in most other respects its performance was identical. The IS-2 had mounted a secondary armament of one 12.7 mm or 7.62 mm anti-aircraft machine-gun, one 7.62 mm co-axial machine-gun and one 7.62 mm in the rear wall of the turret, but the last was sensibly dispensed with in the IS-3.

It is doubtful whether the IS-3 saw anything more than limited action in 1945 as it began reaching the heavy regiments about the time hostilities ended. The Western Allies had their first view of the vehicle during the joint Victory Parade held in Berlin that September and the fact that they had nothing comparable in their own armouries made them take it extremely seriously. Their reaction was to design short-

Overleaf:
The function of the Russian heavy tanks was either to shoot in an attack or form its leading wave. Often infantry could be carried aboard the tanks to the assault start-line—hence the grab handles welded to this IS-3's turret. Note the elliptical plate welded to the hull just below the turret, the purpose of which was to prevent explosive devices being lodged in the pronounced overhang *(Novosti)*.

lived heavy tanks of their own, notably the American M103 and the British Conqueror, both of which were armed with a 120 mm gun, from which useful experience was gained. Concurrently, the Soviet Army set about improving the IS-3 design in a number of ways and in 1952 the IS-10 was standardised and accepted for production, although following Stalin's death the following year the political climate was such that its title was promptly changed to T-10.

In this version more internal space and a marginally improved ammunition stowage capacity had been achieved by stretching the hull, which was carried on seven pairs of roadwheels instead of six, and by fitting a larger turret. A further improvement was the provision of a fume extractor, fitted to the gun just behind the muzzle brake. The T-10 weighed 50.8 tonnes (50 UK tons, 46 US tons) and was powered by the same type of diesel engine as the IS-3, up-rated to 700 hp at 2,000 rpm, producing a maximum speed of 42 km/h (26 mph). Further improvements followed in

The T-10 differs from the IS-3 in having seven roadwheels, a fume extractor fitted to the barrel and a slotted muzzle brake.

24

1957 with the T-10M, which saw the substitution of a five-baffle for the double-baffle muzzle brake, while a heavy 14.5 mm machine-gun replaced the 12.7 mm weapon in the anti-aircraft role. In its final form the tank was equipped with main armament stabilisation, infrared (IR) night fighting and driving aids, a pressurised Nuclear-Biological-Chemical (NBC) defence system and a schnorkel tube for deep fording.

It is estimated that some 6,000 heavy tanks were built in Russia after 1945, although they saw only limited active service. Some IS-3 units were present in Budapest in 1956 and at least one T-10M unit took part in the occupation of Prague in 1968. The IS-3 was supplied to the Egyptian Army which used it to support its frontier defences during the Six Day War of 1967 but it proved unequal to the sort of fast-moving battle imposed by the Israelis with their Centurions and Pattons.

The engagements of the Six-Day War, especially that at Rafah, merely emphasised what the Soviet Army already knew, namely that the heavy tank had had its day. Gun and ammunition technology had advanced so rapidly that the performance of the now-elderly 122 mm weapon was inferior to that of the 115 mm gun which armed the T-62 medium tank, while the British L7 105 mm gun adopted by NATO armies was quite capable of penetrating the armour of the IS-3 and T-10 at long range. Further, the lower speed of the heavy tanks rendered them incompatible with the sort of high-mobility operations for which the latest generation of Russian main battle tanks had been designed. By 1967 the process of withdrawing them from first line service was in hand, although large numbers of chassis were converted for use as missile carriers.

Although the gap in the standard of secondary technical education which existed between the Soviet Union and the West during World War 2 has undoubtedly closed with the passing of the years, the first Russian tank designs to be produced after 1945 reflected the need for simple, uncomplicated, robust vehicles on which large numbers of men from widely differing cultural and ethnic backgrounds could be trained quickly and efficiently. The term most appropriate to such designs is soldier-proof and it is this very quality, coupled with a cheap unit cost guaranteed by long production runs, which has ensured such a ready market for Soviet tanks around the world. The description certainly fits the T-54/55 series and since some estimates suggest that as many as 70,000 of these vehicles have been constructed in various forms this alone merits the tank's place as one of the most important designs ever built.

As early as 1945 it was appreciated that not only could the 85 mm gun of the T-34/85 and T-44 no longer be regarded as adequate against the armour carried by the British Centurion and the American M26, but also that the West was developing more powerful guns for its new generation of medium tanks which were superior to anything which had been encountered during the Great Patriotic War. The situation, therefore, possessed an urgency not immediately apparent to Western observers, who remained in awe of the T-34/85 until the Korean War, and of the IS-3 for some years longer.

The choice of gun fell upon a former naval weapon, the 100 mm L/54 which already armed the SU-100 tank destroyer. This was fitted experimentally to a T-44 and while considered satisfactory in itself it was appreciated that a larger turret—and hence a larger turret ring—was required to absorb the gun's recoil and provide adequate room for the handling of the bigger round. The prototype T-54 was produced in 1946 and manufacture commenced the following year.

The hull and torsion bar suspension were inherited directly from the T-44, cushioned by hydraulic shock absorbers above the first and fifth roadwheels. However, the Christie method of engagement between the final drive and the track, which had been retained on the T-44, was replaced by a conventional rear drive-sprocket. Conversely, a curious survival from the T-34 was the wiper-plate method of track-pin retention. An aid to fording was a splash-plate mounted horizontally across the glacis.

A dome-shaped cast turret was adopted with a small roof section welded in; on the first batch of T-54 turrets to be completed a pronounced rear overhang was evident, but this was quickly eliminated. Separate hatches were provided for the loader and commander, the latter's cupola being capable of all-round rotation. An electro-hydraulic power traverse system with manual back-up was installed, 21 seconds being required to complete the cycle. The main armament possessed an elevation of +21 degrees but a depression of only −4 degrees. Thirty-four rounds of main armament ammunition were stowed, the bulk in a rack located on the driver's right, directly beneath the glacis. Secondary armament consisted of one 12.7 mm machine-gun for anti-aircraft defence, mounted above the loader's hatch, and two 7.62 mm machine-guns, one mounted co-axially with the main armament and the other, operated by the driver, in a fixed mounting in the bow. The glacis plate was 97 mm (3.8 in) thick and laid back at 58 degrees, while the mantlet was 203 mm (8 in) thick. The tank weighed 36.6 tonnes (36 UK tons, 33 US tons) and was powered by the usual type of Russian V-12 water-cooled diesel engine with an output of 520 hp at 2,000 rpm, producing a maximum speed of 50 km/h (31 mph). It was crewed by commander, gunner, loader and driver.

This, then, was the basic T-54 which was to evolve more or less continuously throughout the next 20 years. The first major improvement took place during the early 1950s with the introduction of main armament stabilisation in

An early model T-54 medium tank, identified by the turret's rear overhang and the 'clean' barrel (*US Army*).

On later models of the T-54 the rear overhang was eliminated. These vehicles were photographed in Magyarover, Hungary, during the Soviet invasion of 1956 (*Associated Press*).

The T-54's 100 mm gun was slightly breech-heavy and after vertical stabilisation was installed in later models a counter-weight was fitted to the muzzle to restore balance.

Hungarian crewmen practise their bale-out drill from a T-54B. This version was equipped with infrared night fighting and driving aids. From 1955 onwards a fume extractor was fitted as standard behind the muzzle of the main armament, dispensing with the need for a counter-weight.

A crew from the same
unit re-ammunitioning
their vehicle.

the vertical plane; as the gun was slightly breech-heavy, this required the fitting of a small counter-weight to the muzzle to restore balance. This was itself rendered superfluous in 1955 when a fume extractor was fitted to the barrel just behind the muzzle, a very necessary step since after a round had been fired previously most of the fumes would trickle back into the turret, inducing nausea and exhaustion in the loader, who was already trying to perform his heavy task crouched in extremely cramped surroundings with scant headroom. In this form the tank was designated T-54A.

The T-54B began appearing in 1957 and incorporated further improvements, including main armament stabilisation in the horizontal plane. Infrared night-fighting equipment was also fitted, consisting of a 1,000 m (1,094 yd) light projector mounted co-axially with the gun, a smaller 400 m (437 yd) light projector in a flexible mounting forward of the commander's cupola, and a passive night-driving periscope for the driver with a range of approximately 60 m (65 yd). The T-54C saw the temporary removal of the anti-aircraft machine-gun and the replacement of the loader's cupola by a flush hatch.

The T-54 series can ford without preparation to a depth of 1.4 m (4 ft 7 in) but after proofing can complete a submerged river crossing with the aid of a schnorkel tube fitted

to a ventilator just forward of the loader's hatch; this takes about 30 minutes to erect and can be blown off on reaching the far bank. During training a much wider tube is fixed directly to the loader's hatch and also serves as an escape route in case of accident.

Another point of interest is the vehicle's ability to lay a dense screen of white smoke by injecting fuel into the left exhaust when hot. This lasts about two minutes before dispersing. When advancing tactically the leading wave of tanks make smoke simultaneously once they are within the enemy's range, thereby preventing him from engaging succeeding waves.

The next progression in the series was the T-55, which is believed to have entered service in the late 1950s but which first appeared on parade in 1961. The vehicle is almost indistinguishable from the T-54 series save that the mushroom vent cover located forward of the loader's hatch on the latter has disappeared. On the other hand, there were a large number of internal improvements, including a pressurised NBC defence system with gamma ray sensor. The engine had been up-rated to 580 hp at 2,000 rpm and a power-assisted clutch installed, lessening driver fatigue. Internal fuel capacity had been increased from 532 to 680 litres (117 to 150 gallons) and nine more rounds of main armament ammunition could be stowed. The T-55 also incorporated a revolving turret floor, a provision most appreciated by the loader who had previously been in serious danger of injury from the movements of the breech if the stabiliser was engaged. Further improvements followed in the T-55A, which appeared in 1963. Most notable of these was additional anti-radiation protection for the crew compartments in the form of foam-backed lead panels. This version dispensed with the bow machine-gun.

The T-54/T-55 series was built not only in the Soviet Union but also in Czechoslovakia and Poland, with such minor differences as the type and location of external stowage bins in the latter case. The T-54 was also built in the People's Republic of China under the designation of T-59. The Rumanian Army has radically modified its T-54/T-55 fleet by stretching the hull and incorporating an additional pair of roadwheels as well as fitting side-skirts in the British manner, the local designation of this vehicle being the M-77. Numerous T-54s and T-55s were captured by the Israeli Defence Force during the wars of 1967 and 1973, many being re-armed with the British L7 105 mm gun. The Egyptian Army is also seriously considering up-gunning its own T-55s to this standard, the Royal Ordnance Factories having developed a kit for this specific purpose.

Despite its long service and continuous development, recognition of the various models within the T-54/T-55 series is an inexact science, particularly at long range, partly because the essential external features have remained substantially unchanged, and partly because when Soviet tanks are returned to factories for a complete overhaul after every 7,000 km (4,375 miles) of use, they undergo a total retrospective modification to bring them up to date, worn original features such as early pattern roadwheels being also replaced from modern stock. In some cases the likeness between cousins is too close for comfort. The Indian Army, for example, was forced to add dummy sheet metal tubing 'fume extractors' to the guns of its T-54s and T-55s, simulating the L7 105 mm gun, in order to distinguish its

T-55s of a Polish tank company on exercise
(*Wojskowa Agencja Fotograficzna*).

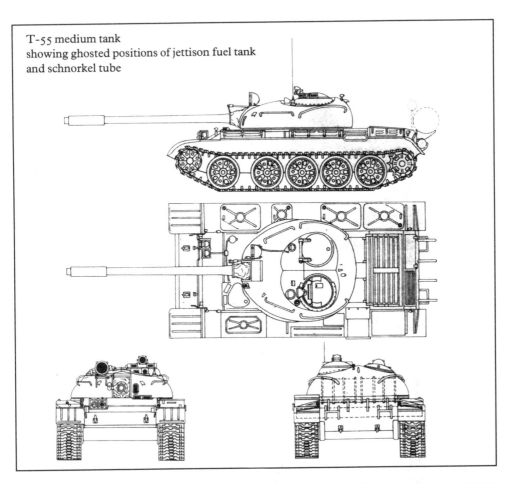

T-55 medium tank
showing ghosted positions of jettison fuel tank
and schnorkel tube

View from the
commander's seat
across the breech of the
T-54/T-55's 100 mm gun
to the loader's position,
showing the recoil
buffers and breech
mechanism lever. The
picture emphasises the
very limited headroom
available (*RAC Tank
Museum*).

Loader's view, looking forward to the ready-use ammunition rack, co-axial machine-gun mounting and ammunition tray. The difficulty involved in handling large rounds in this confined space can well be imagined (*RAC Tank Museum*).

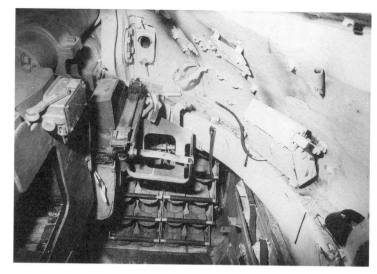

Gunner's position showing manual elevation and traverse controls, power traverse handle and details of the main armament mounting (*RAC Tank Museum*).

Looking down into the turret interior from the commander's cupola (*RAC Tank Museum*).

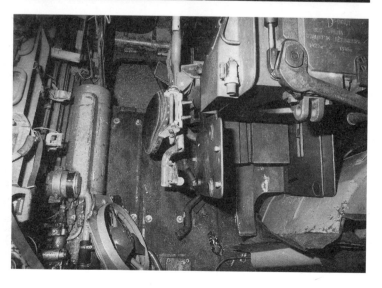

View of the turret interior from the driving compartment. The gunner's folding stool is in the foreground (*RAC Tank Museum*).

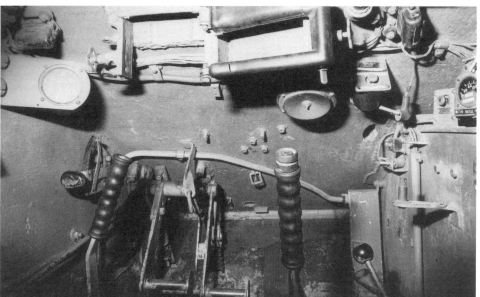

Driving compartment showing steering levers, foot controls and gear lever (*RAC Tank Museum*).

T-55 gunner peers into his telescopic sight.

T-55 loader punches home a 100 mm round.

Crossing water obstacles forms a regular part of the Warsaw Pact's training schedules. Here a powered raft embarks the leading tank of a T-54 company for a river crossing.

If the river bed is suitable and the banks permit entry and exit, tanks can drive across submerged with the aid of a schnorkel tube which is fitted to a ventilator just forward of the loader's hatch. On reaching the far bank the schnorkel is blown off.

During training a much wider tube is fixed directly to the loader's hatch and provides an escape route in case of accidents.

The T-54/T-55 series can also ford without preparation to a depth of 1.4 m (4 ft 7 in.), although in this case the mantlets have been sealed with waterproof sheeting. The exercise is being carried out under live ammunition conditions with all hatches closed *(Novosti)*.

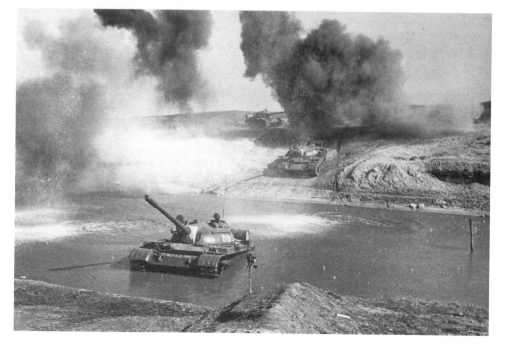

tanks from the dangerously similar T-59s in the service of Pakistan.

A flamethrower version of the T-55 exists, the flame gun being mounted co-axially with the main armament and to its right; it is said to have an effective range of approximately 150 m (164 yd). Several turretless armoured recovery vehicles (ARVs) have been based on the T-54/T-55 chassis, the most common being the T-54-T, which is equipped with a jib crane, rear spade and spare parts deck. The series also forms the basis of a number of assault engineer vehicles including bridge-layers, mineclearers and a purpose-built combat engineer tractor, which are more fully discussed in Chapter 9. At the local level it is, of course, possible to fit a dozer blade quickly to a gun tank that is otherwise unadapted.

The T-55 ended its remarkable production run in 1979, although it is thought that some residual capacity has been retained for the benefit of export clients. As well as serving in the armies of the Soviet Union and her Warsaw Pact allies, the T-54/T-55 series can also be found in the armies of Afghanistan, Albania, Algeria, Angola, Bangladesh, the Central African Republic, China, Congo (T-59), Cuba, Cyprus, Egypt, Equatorial Guinea, Ethiopia, Finland, Guinea, Guinea-Bissau, India, Iraq, Israel, North Korea (T-59), Libya, Mali, Mongolia, Morocco, Mozambique, Nicaragua, Nigeria, Pakistan (T-59), Peru, Somalia, Syria, Yemen, South Yemen, Yugoslavia, Vietnam, Zambia and Zimbabwe.

Tempting as it might be to regard the original T-62 concept as a fusion of the T-54/T-55 medium tank series with the long-range engagement capacity of the now-obsolete IS-3/T-10 heavy tanks to produce an all-purpose main battle tank (MBT), this is really something of an over-simplification. Nor is it altogether quite accurate to say that the tank was conceived as a replacement for the T-55, which actually remained in production for some time after the last T-62 had been built. In fact, although the T-62 did eventually assume the role of an MBT, the initial intention was that it should serve in parallel with the T-55 regiments in units which replaced the tank division's heavy tank/tank destroyer regiments which had had the task of shooting in the medium tanks' attack and picking off enemy armour at long range.

By the late 1950s it was becoming painfully apparent that the T-55's 100 mm gun was unable to penetrate the frontal armour of the Centurion and the M48 Patton at the standard battle-range of 1,000 m (1,094 yd) with kinetic energy armour-piercing (AP) ammunition, which relied on the speed of its delivery to obtain its effect. It was certainly possible to achieve the desired result by employing shaped-charge rounds such as HEAT (High Explosive Anti-Tank), as the chemical energy released could blast a hole through the thickest armour then in service; this, however, would have meant a radical re-structuring of the gunnery training programme as AP ammunition is fired at a high muzzle velocity and flies in a flat trajectory while HEAT ammunition is fired at a much lower velocity and travels in a sharply curved trajectory, making target acquisition that much more difficult, especially at long range. At this period Russian gunsights and range-finding techniques were still comparatively unsophisticated, so that the adoption of HEAT as the main armour-defeating round would have entailed far more live-firing

115 mm APFSDS (Armour-Piercing Fin-Stabilised Discarding-Sabot) rounds stowed aboard a T-62 main battle tank.

training than was required, or permitted, with AP ammunition, thereby incurring an astronomic increase in expenditure which not even the Soviet Army was prepared to justify. It was decided, therefore, that kinetic energy would remain the principal method of penetrating the enemy's armour in the tank *v.* tank battle and the question now became one of finding a weapon system powerful enough for the task.

In the past Russian tank designers had been able to rely on guns which were also widely used as towed field artillery, anti-tank and anti-aircraft guns, and aboard naval vessels. They were now forced to take what for them almost amounted to a step in the dark in adopting a 115 mm L/50 smooth-bore weapon which had entered production as a towed anti-tank gun as recently as 1955. This fired an Armour-Piercing Fin-Stabilised Discarding-Sabot (APFSDS) round at a muzzle-velocity of 1,615 m (5,300 ft) per second, giving it the ability to penetrate any NATO tank in service at 1,500 m (1,640 yd). The round consists of a sub-calibre steel penetrator enclosed in a sabot. On leaving the muzzle the sabot disintegrates but the penetrator retains the kinetic energy absorbed, while simultaneously fins maintain the stability in flight that would normally be provided by spinning had the projectile been fired from a rifled barrel. The 115 mm APFSDS round can penetrate 300 mm (11.8 in) vertical armour at 1,000 m (1,094 yd), but beyond 1,500 m (1,640 yd) both its power and accuracy deteriorate rapidly.

The tank version of the 115 mm gun was designated U-5T and was first fitted experimentally to a T-55. This proved to be the inverse of the KV-1's problem, namely a case of too much gun for too little tank. Clearly a larger turret and turret ring were necessary to absorb the heavier recoil, which in turn meant a larger hull in which provision had also to be made for stowing an adequate number of the larger rounds. Despite this, the T-62 was based on the T-55 and employed many of the latter's components, including wheels, suspension, tracks, hatch covers and engine, the most obvious external differences being the adoption of a flatter, elipse-shaped turret, a fume extractor mounted two-thirds of the way along the barrel, the disappearance of the large gap between the first and second roadwheels, and extended spacing between the third and fourth and fourth and fifth roadwheels. The T-62 also employs the same night-fighting aids

and NBC protection as the T-55 and possesses the same ability to schnorkel and lay its own smoke screen. Turret front armour is 242 mm (9.5 in) thick and the 102 mm (4 in) glacis plate is laid back at 60 degrees. The tank weighs 37 tonnes (36.5 UK tons, 33.6 US tons) and has a maximum road speed of 50 km/h (31 mph).

The gun is fitted with a stabiliser and possesses electro-hydraulic power controls with manual back-up for the gunner, plus an additional power traverse facility for the commander. Elevation amounts to +17 degrees and depression to −4 degrees. Forty rounds of main armament ammunition can be stowed. In earlier designs, whether or not their main armament was fitted with a fume extractor, fumes had still tended to build up within the turret from expended ammunition cases, which also cluttered the floor and further impeded the loader. In the T-62 an attempt was made to solve both problems simultaneously by providing a hatch in the rear wall of the turret through which the spent cases would be ejected automatically when the breech opened during the gun's recoil. Unfortunately the system lacks an accuracy commensurate with its velocity so that when the case fails to eject cleanly it bounces off the armour, bruising and burning at least one member of the turret crew; the commander seems to be most at risk and a deflection shield has been installed to protect him. To assist the loader in his task the gun automatically goes into an elevation of +3 degrees after it has been fired, the lowered breech making for easier chambering of the next round. The risk potential involved in this was apparent during the design phase and a safety system was installed which simultaneously cuts power to the gun controls, including the stabiliser, enabling the re-load sequence to proceed without the danger of the loader being crushed by unanticipated movements of the breech. Once the sequence has been completed the loader trips the safety switch, restoring power, and if the stabiliser is in use during the engagement the gun will automatically be returned to the correct lay. Although a higher output is claimed, the T-62's rate of fire is approximately four rounds per minute. Later models were fitted with a box-like laser rangefinder mounted above the gun barrel, as were the later T-55s.

The tank's secondary armament consists of a co-axial 7.62 mm machine-gun, but the only

Soviet attacks rely on speed and mass to achieve the desired breakthrough. Here a T-62 company demonstrates the technique during a live ammunition demonstration.

During the desperate fighting on the Golan in October 1973 this Syrian T-62 broke into the Israeli command complex at Nafekh before being knocked out *(Eshel Dramit Ltd)*.

major modification to the basic design, the T-62A, was the installation of a 12.7 mm anti-aircraft machine-gun in a cupola which replaced the loader's hatch, the general re-introduction of such weapons throughout the Soviet armoured corps being a recognition of the fact that in future the helicopter would play an increasingly important role in the land battle.

A command version of the T-62 has been produced, incorporating additional communications equipment and an inertial navigation system. There is also a flamethrower version which employs the same weapon as the T-55 flamethrower.

The T-62 entered its ten-year production run in 1961 and made its public debut in May 1965. The tank was built in Russia and Czechoslovakia and as numbers became available it was issued on a far wider basis than had originally been envisaged. Although still extensively used, it has never achieved the ubiquity of the T-54/T-55 series among the Soviet Union's clients. One reason for this is the much higher unit cost generated by the far shorter production run; initially, the price of a T-62 was US $172,500, or $2\frac{1}{2}$ times that of a T-55, although the gap may have narrowed considerably since. Secondly, in 1968 a Hyper-Velocity Armour-Piercing Discarding-Sabot (HVAPDS) round was introduced for the T-55's 100 mm gun, and as this was capable of penetrating 264 mm (10.4 in) of vertical armour at 1,000 m (1,094 yd), the slight shortfall in comparison with the performance of the 115 mm APFSDS round did not seem to warrant such additional heavy expenditure. Thirdly, no sooner had the T-62 entered service than it was overtaken by the next generation of NATO MBTs, including the heavily armoured Chieftain, which mounted a 120 mm gun, and the American M60; it was also shortly apparent that the T-62 was far slower than the new Soviet infantry fighting vehicle, the BMP, with which it would have to operate. All of these factors indicated that the design of a new Soviet MBT was imperative and thus made long-term investment in the T-62 a poor proposition.

As well as serving in the Soviet and Czecho-slovakian Armies, the T-62 has also been supplied to Afghanistan, Angola, Algeria, Bulgaria, Cuba, Egypt, Ethiopia, East Germany, Iraq, Libya, Mongolia, Mozambique, North Korea, Rumania, Syria, South Yemen, Vietnam and Yugoslavia. It took part in some of the heaviest fighting of the 1973 Yom Kippur War, both on the Golan Heights and the Sinai front, but fared badly despite the desperate bravery shown by the majority of its crews. The Israelis, who captured many, were impressed by the technical performance of the 115 mm gun but commented adversely on its low rate of fire and the lack of depression available, which had particularly inhibited the Egyptians during the great tank battles of 14 October.

The problems facing the designers of the T-62's successor were as urgent as they were formidable, for not only had they to provide something better than parity in firepower with the newest generation of NATO MBTs, and specifically the Chieftain, they were also required to increase the tank's mobility to the point at which it was compatible with the BMP armoured personnel carrier (APC) and simultaneously incorporate protection against the wide variety of shaped charge ammunition with which the NATO armies were so extensively equipped, including tank and artillery rounds, Anti-Tank Guided Weapon (ATGW) missile systems, and short-range tube-launched infantry anti-tank weapons. Moreover, unlike their NATO counterparts, who were permitted considerable latitude in the size and weight of their product, Soviet designers were bound by inflexible strategic parameters which continued to emphasise the need for small, compact, simple and robust medium tanks with a high mobility factor. The difficulty in reconciling these diverse requirements was fully appreciated and it now seems certain that the unusual step was taken of employing two design bureaux to explore alternative lines of development, there being general agreement that the evolutionary line T-44/T-55/T-62 had at last exhausted its potential.

The common point of departure for both new designs was a 125 mm L/45 version of the 115 mm smoothbore gun which armed the T-62. Given the larger ammunition required for this weapon and the mandatory limits imposed on the size of the tank, it was soon apparent that if a four-man crew was retained stowage would be limited to a mere 25 rounds. It was therefore decided to dispense with the loader and install an auto-loader in his place. This consisted of a 24-round two-tier carousel mounted on the turret floor, the lower tier containing the projectiles and the upper the matching propellant cases, the latter being combustible save for the base plate. Once the commander has selected the type of ammu-

nition he intends to use, arms extract the projectile and propellant and they are rammed into the breech. During the loading sequence the gun returns to a fixed elevation coincident with the rammer. When the auto-loader is fully operational it is said to be capable of a rate of fire of eight rounds per minute, but such systems carry their own risk of breakdown because of hard usage or inherent defect, and although the gunner can load manually if required to do so, the task is extremely awkward and in consequence the rate of fire drops to one round per minute. In its early years the moving parts of the auto-loader could snatch at the gunner and even drag him into the mechanism, and there are reports of men being killed or sustaining horrifying injuries in this way, but it is probable that further incidents of this nature have been prevented by the installation of a protective shield. When the carousel stock has been depleted it can be replenished with a further 16 rounds which are stowed beside the driver.

The gun is stabilised and has an elevation of + 18 degrees and a depression of − 5 degrees. Powered gun controls are provided for the gunner and commander, with manual back-up for the former, and both have the ability to fire the main armament and the co-axial machine-gun. The first batch of tanks to be delivered were fitted with a coincidence rangefinder, but a laser rangefinder was added subsequently. The gun's final lay is determined by a ballistic computer after the range and other data such as ammunition type have been fed in. Night fighting and driving aids are improved versions of those fitted to the T-62.

Superficially, therefore, the designers appear to have solved their firepower problem in a most ingenious way. On the other hand, as is often the case with Soviet AFV designs, the advantage gained is reflected in the man/machine interface. There is more to crewing an MBT than improved gunnery and it is generally accepted as being a four-man job. The heaviest physical work, that of replenishing fuel and ammunition, general vehicle mainten-

The T-64 main battle tank represented a major departure from the mainstream of Soviet tank design, its 125 mm gun being served by an autoloader. Two schnorkel tubes, one for the engine and the other for the turret, are stowed one inside the other on brackets behind the turret. Some versions, like this example, are fitted with batteries of smoke grenade dischargers on either side of the turret (*US Army*).

ance and running repairs, takes place at the end of the day when everyone is already tired out. If the tank is commanded by an officer, i.e. the company commander and the platoon leaders, the remaining three crew members can share his workload between them while he is absent at orders groups or for other reasons. But if their number is reduced to two serious problems begin to arise because of the very human tendency to cut corners, this being quickly reflected in a rise in the breakdown rate; and if corners are not cut the cumulative effects of lost sleep soon become evident in deteriorating performance. Insofar as protracted operations are concerned this must be regarded as an Achilles' heel, although one to which an answer exists in the regular relief of units.

The first of the two new Soviet tanks to enter service was the T-64, which commenced production in 1967. The project had its roots in a trials vehicle, the T-67, combining a T-62 turret on an experimental hydro-mechanical chassis. Subsequently the 125 mm gun in an enlarged turret was mounted on the same chassis, the combination being designated M-1970 in this prototype form before being standardised as the T-64. The chassis is markedly different from anything that has been seen before in Soviet service, incorporating six

small steel-tyred roadwheels with prominent shock absorbers and four return rollers, the track being of the double-pin rubber-bushed type. The diesel engine, too, is a complete departure from the normal V-series, consisting of a five-cylinder horizontally opposed unit with an output of 700/750 hp capable of producing a maximum road speed of 70 km/h (44 mph). A synchromesh gearbox with seven forward and one reverse gears is employed, inducing less driver fatigue than earlier double de-clutch transmissions, and steering is of the clutch and brake type. Prominent hull details include the shallow angle of the glacis plate, which is ribbed and incorporates a V-shaped splashboard, and a series of small sprung side plates which protect the hull from the full effects of shaped-charge ammunition. Two deep-fording schnorkel tubes, one for the engine and the other for the turret, are stowed one inside the other transversely behind the turret.

As might be expected in a vehicle which departs from tradition in so radical a way, the layout of the T-64 is very different from that of its predecessors. Of the three-man crew, only the gunner remains in the same position he occupied in earlier designs, on the left of the gun. The commander, equipped with a much-

Details of the T-64's suspension, which employs six small steel-tyred roadwheels mounted on torsion bars with hydraulic shock absorbers for the first, second, fifth and sixth wheel stations. The boxes mounted on the turret are for stowage.

improved cupola which allows him to fire the anti-aircraft machine-gun from under cover, occupies the right-rear of the turret, and the driver is seated on the vehicle's centre-line.

The thickness of the tank's armour is estimated as being 280 mm (11 in) on the turret front and 200 mm (7.9 in) on the glacis, but this is not the whole story. Because of NATO's superiority in shaped-charge weapon systems, Soviet scientists and engineers have been working on what they call combined armour since approximately 1961 and this has apparently been incorporated in the design, particularly on the frontal areas. Whatever its precise nature, it is unlike the British-designed Chobham armour, which is worked in slabs, but from its description it probably contains a ceramic element which is capable of resisting and dispersing the jet of high temperature gases and molten metal generated by the explosion of a shaped-charge warhead. Use of such armour, however, does not grant the vehicle an immunity to high-velocity kinetic energy ammunition; and as normal steel armour is employed on its side and upper surfaces these remain vulnerable to attack from those quarters with shaped-charge rounds delivered either by ground troops or tank-hunting helicopters. NBC protection for the crew is comparable to that of the T-62 and also incorporates foam-backed lead plates.

In its standard form the tank is known as the T-64A. An attempt to replace the main armament with a gun/missile launcher system known as *Kobra*, similar to the American Shillelagh, met with only limited success but was produced in sufficient numbers to warrant

the designation T-64B. A command version of the standard gun tank is designated T-64K.

Despite—or, perhaps, because of—the fact that in so many ways the T-64 represented so major an advance in Soviet design philosophy, in its early years it was a mine of trouble. The problems encountered with the auto-loader have already been mentioned, but in addition the fire control system proved unreliable, there were frequent suspension failures and breakdowns were a regular occurrence. At one point technical teams from the manufacturing plant became semi-permanent residents with units equipped with the tank. Even after most of the faults had been cured the T-64 did not serve outside the Soviet Army. Manufacture of the vehicle was discontinued in 1981.

The second new tank, the T-72, entered production in 1971 but was not seen by Western observers until 1977. Its general layout, armour and gunnery equipment are comparable with those of the T-64, but in other respects its designers have followed more traditional paths. The major areas of difference lay, first, in the use of a torsion bar suspension with six medium-sized, rubber-tyred roadwheels and three return rollers, and secondly in the choice of a turbocharged version of the well-tried V-12 diesel engine, capable of producing 780 hp at 3,000 rpm. Minor points of difference between the two types include a slightly larger engine deck on the T-72, a single schnorkel tube stowed on the left side of the turret, the location of the main infrared searchlight to the right of the main armament (as opposed to the left on the T-64), and a pintle mounting for the anti-aircraft machine-

The T-72 main battle tank possesses the same armament and gunnery equipment as the T-64 but in other respects was developed along more traditional lines, as the retention of medium-sized rubber-tyred roadwheels demonstrates. The schnorkel tube is mounted on brackets on the left side of the turret (*US Army*).

T-72 on parade in Red Square, Moscow, to honour the 60th anniversary of the October Revolution. The coincidence rangefinder can be seen running across the turret below the commander's cupola. The laurel wreath, red star and banner insignia denotes a Guards formation (*Novosti*).

T-74 main battle tank

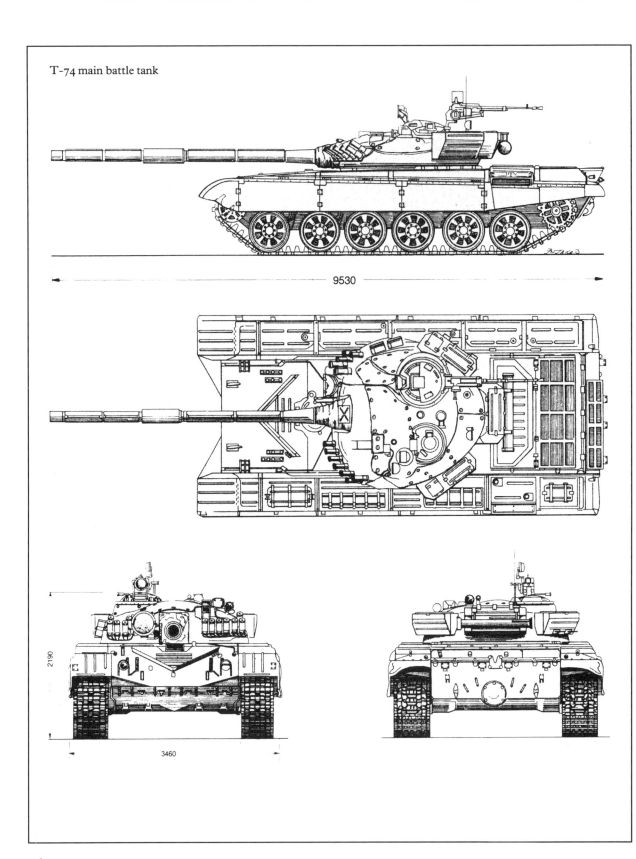

9530

2190

3460

46

A column of T-72s
passes through a
simulated minefield gap
during a misty dawn.
The cleared lane is
marked by striped poles
fitted with lights for use
during the hours of
darkness; on active
service these would
normally be shaded
towards the enemy side
of the gap.

T-72 with schnorkel
tube erected and
thermal jacket fitted to
the main armament.

gun, which can no longer be fired by remote control but has improved elevation. Although not apparent at long range, the T-72 turret has an egg-shaped configuration, while that of the T-64 is rounded. The T-72 weighs 41.65 tonnes (41 UK tons, 37.8 US tons) and has a maximum road speed of 70 km/h (44 mph).

A number of progressive modifications have been incorporated in the T-72 design and these were standardised as the T-74, which first appeared on parade in November 1981. This vehicle dispensed with the coincidence range-finder, was fitted with a battery of forward-firing smoke-grenade dischargers on either side of the turret, and was equipped with a fabric armour skirt in place of the hinged side-plates as a defence against the sub-calibre armour-piercing ammunition fired by the heavy automatic weapons of the majority of NATO's Infantry Fighting Vehicles (IFVs).

The T-72 series is built at three major tank plants inside the USSR and is manufactured under licence in Czechoslovakia and Poland. It is in service with the Warsaw Pact armies and also those of Algeria, Cuba, India, Iraq, Libya, Syria and Yugoslavia. It has seen limited active service in Afghanistan and was encountered in the Beka'a Valley during the 1982 Israeli invasion of Lebanon, when a number of Syrian T-72s were knocked out both by tanks and by other means. The Israelis were favourably impressed by the design and in particular by its low silhouette which enabled it to take advantage of the limited cover afforded by the terrain.

In essence, however, while offering increased reliability and other improvements on the T-64, the T-72/T-74 remains a small three-man MBT served by an auto-loader. It has achieved parity in a number of critical areas with the British Chieftain, the American M60 and the German Leopard 1, but these vehicles are now being replaced by far more advanced designs in the shape of, respectively, the Challenger, the M1 Abrams and the Leopard 2. Again, while offering more sophisticated gunnery equipment than any previous Soviet tank, it is probably fair to question whether this can equal the results produced by the Improved Fire Control System (IFCS) and similar high-technology computerised systems which have been installed in NATO MBTs.

The T-74 is equipped with a battery of smoke grenade dischargers on either side of the gun and a fabric skirt protects the upper part of the suspension. These examples carry East German markings.

There therefore appears to be a half-generation gap between the T-72/T-74 series and their NATO counterparts. On the other hand, Russian designers have hardly been idle during the past twenty years and it is more than probable that a new MBT, given the provisional designation 'T-80' in the West, is already serving with selected units within the Soviet Union. If past experience is any guide, this will only be unveiled to the world during the celebration of some significant event, such as an important anniversary of the Bolshevik coup. As to the form the vehicle will take, there is a general belief that the Russians are satisfied with the 125 mm gun and are prepared to tolerate some increase in weight; this suggests that as well as improving the fire control system, they will concentrate on an increased protection factor, simultaneously up-rating the engine to cope with the additional load. Reports claim that the 'T-80' has the appearance of the T-72 but with some angled surfaces on the turret, so hinting at the incorporation of Chobham-type armour in its construction.

Implicit in the Soviet Army's declared intention of fighting any future war on the enemy's territory was the need for a light tank with an amphibious capability which could perform the reconnaissance role without being inhibited by the numerous water obstacles which would be encountered, and as the World War 2 light tank series had exhausted its development potential the task of designing such a vehicle was given to the Kotin bureau shortly after the war ended. This produced the prototype PT-76 (*Plavuchii Tank* or Swimming Tank) in

1952 and three years later the vehicle entered general service.

The PT-76 weighs 14.2 tonnes (14 UK tons, 12.9 US tons) and is powered by a six-cylinder in-line diesel engine producing 240 hp at 1,800 rpm, this being simply one bank of the standard V-12 medium tank engine. The running gear consists of six roadwheels mounted on a torsion bar suspension, front idler and rear drive sprocket. Steering is by means of clutch and brake and a synchromesh transmission provides five forward and one reverse gears.

PT-76 amphibious light tank. The slotted muzzle brake indicates an early production model. The white stripes are air recognition markings (*US Army*).

On later models the gun was fitted with a fume extractor and double-baffle muzzle brake *(Novosti).*

Maximum road speed obtainable is 44 km/h (27.5 mph).

The only preparation required before the vehicle enters the water is the erection of the trim vane mounted on the front of the hull. Propulsion when afloat is by means of two powerful hydrojets which emerge from ports in the stern plate. Steering is obtained by means of varying the intake to each hydrojet, although the results are far from precise. The engine compartment is fitted with two electric bilge pumps, with a manual pump backup. Even so, because of the tank's low freeboard, the engine is vulnerable to swamping in even moderately disturbed water and a turret-mounted schnorkel is generally used. As the erection of the trim vane severely curtails the driver's vision he is forced to rely on the commander's orders for direction and station-keeping. When afloat, the vehicle has a maximum speed of 10 km/h (6.2 mph).

The PT-76 is a three-man tank, the driver being seated on the vehicle's centre-line, the commander-gunner on the left of the turret and the loader on the right. The tank is armed with a 76.2 mm L/42 gun, an adaption of the same weapon mounted by the T-34/76 and the KV-1, and a 7.62 mm co-axial machine-gun. The main armament has been the subject of progressive modification and distinguishes the various models of the PT-76. On the early versions, known as Model 1, the barrel of the gun was clean but ended in a slotted multi-baffle muzzle brake; on the Model 2 the barrel is fitted with a fume extractor and a double-baffle muzzle brake; on some tanks, often called Model 3, the fume extractor is absent; the Model 4, also designated PT-76B, incorporates a stabiliser. Forty-four rounds of main armament ammunition can be stowed and the maximum rate of fire attainable is 15 rounds per minute. No infrared night-fighting equipment is provided, although the driver has one small infrared headlight. Nor is the tank equipped with NBC protection and detection devices, which might be regarded as surprising in a vehicle intended for the deep reconnaissance role, but in the very limited amount of

A Polish Naval Infantry unit comes ashore during an amphibious exercise in the Baltic. Details of the turret-mounted schnorkel are clearly visible on the leading PT-76; for some reason the muzzle brakes have been removed from the tank guns. In the background are three BTR-50P armoured personnel carriers (*Wojskowa Agencja Fotograficzna*).

The PT-76's twin hydrojets provide powerful propulsion afloat but steering can be erratic (*Novosti*).

internal space available there is clearly a limit to the amount of equipment that can be installed.

The Achilles' heel of the design, as might be expected, lies in its very limited protection, the glacis armour being only 11 mm (0.4 in) thick laid back at 80 degrees, the turret front 17 mm (0.67 in) at 35 degrees, and the vertical hull sides 14 mm (0.55 in). This renders it vulnerable even to low-calibre armour-piercing ammunition fired by heavy automatic weapons, although its built-in flotation tanks provide spaced armour protection which degrades the effect of small hollow-charge rounds such as that fired by the 66 mm LAW (Light Anti-Tank Weapon).

In the Soviet and Warsaw Pact armies the PT-76 formed part of the equipment of the divisional reconnaissance battalions in the tank and motor rifle divisions, and also of the regimental reconnaissance companies in tank and motor rifle regiments, in which it operated in support of the wheeled reconnaissance units. Production has now ceased and the vehicle has been steadily replaced in first line service by the scout version of the BMP, although apparently it remains active in the tank battalions of Naval Infantry regiments. The real legacy of the PT-76, however, is that its chassis has formed the basis of so many other Soviet combat vehicles, including the BTR-50 armoured personnel carrier, the BMP infantry fighting vehicle, the ASU-85 airborne assault gun and several missile carriers. The PT-76 has been widely exported and is in service with the armies of Afghanistan, Angola, Congo, Cuba, Egypt, Finland, Guinea, India, Indonesia, Iraq, Laos, Madagascar, Mozambique, North Korea, Pakistan, Vietnam and Yugoslavia.

Some early models were also delivered to the People's Republic of China, which subsequently produced its own version of the tank, known as the Type 63. This employs a cast domed turret and is armed with an 85 mm gun with fume extractor but no muzzle brake. The engine is a V-12 diesel producing 520 hp at 2,000 rpm and although the vehicle is some four tonnes heavier than the PT-76 it has a higher maximum road speed of 50 km/h (31.25 mph). The Type 63 has a four-man crew, the commander and gunner being located on the left of the gun and the loader on the right, while the driver's position has been moved to the left; this layout, while unbearably cramped,

enables 56 rounds of main armament ammunition to be stowed, the majority under the glacis to the driver's right. The Type 63, often mistakenly reported as being the PT-76, is also used by the armies of Pakistan, the Sudan, Tanzania and Vietnam.

The combat record of the PT-76 includes both successes and failures. It saw action in the Indo-Pakistani wars of 1965 and 1971; on the latter occasion it served the Indians well during their advances into East Pakistan (now Bangladesh) because of its ability to cross the many water obstacles which intersect the country. During the opening moves of the Yom Kippur War PT-76s and BTR-50s of the Egyptian 130th Marine Brigade swam the Great Bitter Lake with the intention of re-inforcing commando units that had been inserted into Sinai by helicopter, but the move was detected and foiled by Israeli armour, which inflicted serious loss on the thin-skinned vehicles. In Vietnam 13 PT-76s spearheaded a surprise night attack which overran the US Special Forces camp at Lang Vei, but elsewhere any attempt to employ the PT-76 or Type 63 against American armour or in the assault role predictably ended in disaster.

The Soviet Army's first post-war wheeled reconnaissance vehicle, the 5.4-tonne (5.3 UK ton, 4.9 US ton) BTR-40, was introduced in 1951. This was a copy of the American White scout car, which it closely resembles, and consists of an angled 8 mm (0.3 in) armour-plate body mounted on a 4 × 4 GAZ-63 lorry chassis. The vehicle is powered by an 80 hp six-cylinder in-line petrol engine and has a maximum road speed of 80 km/h (50 mph). Normal armament is limited to a single 7.62 mm machine-gun for which three alternative pintle mountings are provided in the rear compartment, each giving an elevation of + 23.5 degrees, depression of − 6 degrees and an approximate 90 degree field of fire; the rear compartment also contains protected side and rear ports through which infantry weapons can be used. The vehicle's crew consists of commander and driver.

As well as performing the reconnaissance role, the BTR-40 can also be fitted as a command or communications vehicle and serve as an APC carrying an eight-man infantry section. An air-defence version, armed with twin 14.5 mm heavy machine-guns on a mounting giving all-round traverse, is designated BTR-40A. Later models of the scout

One of two PT-76s of the
North Vietnamese
Army's 202nd
Armoured Regiment
destroyed by M48A3
Pattons during the
former's attack on a US
Special Forces camp at
Ben Het during the
night of 3 March 1969
*(US Army Military
History Institute)*.

This PT-76 was
captured by the South
Vietnamese Army
during the abortive
communist offensive of
1972. The extensive
suspension damage has
been caused by an anti-
tank mine *(USAMHI)*.

In Vietnam the PT-76 was sometimes confused with the Chinese-built Type 63 light tank, although the latter has a domed turret and its 85 mm gun lacks a muzzle brake *(USAMHI)*.

South Vietnamese civilians inspect equipment captured during the failed communist offensive of 1972. The Type 63 light tank nearest the camera bears the insignia of the North Vietnamese Naval Infantry *(USAMHI)*.

The BA-64 was a light scout car of 1942 vintage which remained in service for some years after the Great Patriotic War. The vehicle was normally armed with a 7.62 mm machine-gun housed in a small turret, the mounting ring of which is visible. This example was captured by United Nations troops in Korea (USAMHI).

A posed but interesting study of a BRDM-1 scout car armed with Snapper ATGWs. In the foreground the missile controller holds his joystick control, the remote command wire of which trails back aboard the vehicle. The second crewman is armed with an RPG-7 close-range anti-tank weapon.

car/APC incorporating overhead armour and four roof hatches are designated BTR-40B.

The BTR-40, always regarded as an expedient design, lacks the amphibious capability the Russians demand of their reconnaissance units and it has long been withdrawn from this role by the Warsaw Pact armies although it is still used by Military Police detachments, by NBC reconnaissance training units and, fitted with a retractable roof mounting three Sagger missiles below, by the East German Army as an Anti-Tank Guided Weapon (ATGW) training vehicle. It also remains active in the majority of Soviet-supplied armies around the world.

The BTR-40's immediate successor, the BRDM-1, first appeared in 1959 and although it too relied on many components of the GAZ-63 lorry it was a full design generation ahead of the older vehicle. The BRDM-1, while retaining the same front-mounted engine as the BTR-40, up-rated to 90 hp, is a fully enclosed scout car purpose-built with cross-country performance and amphibious requirements in mind. The vehicle is equipped with a centralised control system which en-

ables the driver to vary the tyre pressure in accordance with the nature of the terrain being crossed, and on really difficult going two pairs of chain-driven small diameter tyred wheels, normally carried centrally in a retracted position, can be lowered to assist its passage. On hard going the BRDM-1 can equal the BTR-40's maximum speed despite being slightly heavier at 5.7 tonnes (5.6 UK tons, 5.1 US tons). A boat-shaped hull enables the vehicle to take to the water without difficulty, the only preparation required being the erection of a trim vane on the bow. When afloat the car is powered by a single hydrojet which makes its exit through the stern plate, the two leading wheels acting as rudders. Maximum speed afloat is 9 km/h (5.6 mph).

The BRDM-1 is manned by a commander and driver, with room for up to three passengers, including a missile operator. Armament consists of a pintle-mounted 12.7 mm or 7.62 mm machine-gun, and occasionally both. This is omitted on those vehicles equipped with retractable ATGW launching racks, of which three types have been fitted: a triple launcher for the Snapper, a quadruple launcher for the

57

BRDM-2 scout car with ATGW launching rack raised *(US Army)*.

Details of Sagger ATGW and sextuple launching rails mounted on BRDM-2 *(Wojskowa Agencja Fotograficzna)*.

Swatter-A and a sextuple launcher for the Sagger. A command version (the BRDM-U) and an NBC reconnaissance version (the BRDM-rkh) of the car have also been produced. The Hungarian FUG or OT-85 scout car in service with the Hungarian, Czechoslovakian and Polish armies is very similar to the BRDM-1, although the engine is mounted at the rear.

Although the BRDM-1 was an ingenious design which remains in service, for the moment, with the Soviet and several other armies, it was soon clear that its potential could be further developed and it was soon overtaken by the BRDM-2, which was first seen in 1966. This retains the centralised tyre pressure controls, retractable ventral wheels and hydrojet propulsion unit, but is driven by a rear-mounted V-8 petrol engine which produces 140 hp at 3,400 rpm, the most obvious result of the new layout being the elimination of the long prow which distinguishes the BRDM-1. Armament consists of a 14.5 mm heavy

machine-gun mounted co-axially with a 7.62 mm machine-gun in a shallow, flat-topped turret with all-round traverse; this is manually controlled and provides an elevation range from + 30 degrees to − 5 degrees. The vehicle is fitted with an infrared searchlight and night driving aids as well as an NBC defence system, the ventilator of which is located behind and to the left of the turret; a proportion are also equipped with a navigation system. The crew consists of commander and driver but a two-man reconnaissance patrol can be transported with weapons and equipment for employment in a dismounted role. The BRDM-2 weighs 7.1 tonnes (7 UK tons, 6.45 US tons) and its maximum speeds are 100 km/h (62.5 mph) on the road and 10 km/h (6.25 mph) when afloat. Frontal armour thickness is 14 mm (0.55 in) as opposed to 10 mm (0.4 in) on the BRDM-1.

Turretless BRDM-2s fitted with retractable launching racks and guidance systems are widely used in the ATGW role, one version mounting six Sagger AT-3s, another four

This BRDM-2, armed with four Gaskin SA-9 surface-to-air missiles mounted on a retractable launching arm, was captured by South African troops in Angola. The triangular hatch in the vehicle's stern plate covers the hydrojet propulsion unit (*South African Army*).

BRDM-2 with ventral wheels lowered *(Eshel Dramit Ltd)*.

Interior view of BRDM-2's lowered ventral wheels showing chain drive *(Eshel Dramit Ltd)*.

Cutaway drawing
showing interior layout
of BRDM-2 scout car.

The Hungarian
PSZH-IV is very similar
to the BRDM-2 but was
developed from the
FUG scout car. The
vehicle is armed with a
14.5 mm heavy
machine-gun mounted
co-axially with a 7.62
mm machine-gun.

In the Hungarian Army the PSZH-IV also serves as a light armoured personnel carrier.

Mil Mi-8 helicopters touch down behind a Hungarian PSZH-IV scout car. Air-landing operations play an increasingly important part in the land battle.

PSZH-IVs of a Hungarian reconnaissance company on the move. The soldier in the foreground is aiming a Grail SA-7 surface-to-air heat-seeking missile.

Swatter-B AT-2s and a third (sometimes designated BRDM-3) five Spandrel AT-5s. Another version is equipped with launching arms for four Gaskin SA-9 Surface-to-Air Missiles (SAMs). There are also command and NBC reconnaissance versions of the car designated BRDM-2U and BRDM-2rkh, and a number of variants equipped with radar and other electronic warfare systems.

BRDM scout cars, including a proportion of NBC reconnaissance vehicles, form the backbone of the divisional reconnaissance battalions and regimental reconnaissance companies in both tank and motor rifle divisions and regiments, and also form part of the equipment of the reconnaissance battalion of Naval Infantry regiments. ATGW versions are most widely used by the motor rifle divisions in which they supplement the towed anti-tank guns in the divisional anti-tank battalion and equip the regimental anti-tank companies and battalion anti-tank platoons in the motor-rifle regiments; in tank divisions they equip the anti-tank company of the motor-rifle regiment. SAM versions are issued to the air defence companies of tank and motor rifle regiments in which they supplement the fire of the ZSU-23-4 self-propelled anti-aircraft guns. The BRDM-2 series is in service with some 40 armies round the world and is still in production.

Soviet wheeled reconnaissance vehicles saw extensive active service during the Arab-Israeli wars. In 1956 the Egyptians used BTR-40s, and in 1967 both Egypt and Syria employed BTR-40s, BRDM-1s and a handful of BRDM-2s. The BRDM-1 and BRDM-2 were again used by Egypt and Syria during the 1973 war, in which they were joined by the Sagger ATGW version of the BRDM-2. In Angola all three basic types are employed by the communist forces and examples of each have been captured by the South African Army during its cross-border strikes.

During the great offensive battles fought by the Soviet Army between 1943 and 1945 the Russian infantry, including designated motor rifle troops, had gone into action on foot or, at best, riding part of the way to their objectives on the back of tanks. It had, therefore, been a comparatively simple matter for the German defence to separate the infantry from their tanks by pinning them down, the effect being that the tanks lacked infantry support when tackling anti-tank gun screens and the infantry lacked the tank support which should have dealt with the bunkers and machine-gun posts that were holding them up. Consequently, even the cost of successful operations tended to be disproportionately high and post-war analysis of these battles confirmed beyond any reasonable doubt that it had been the lack of APCs which had been the greatest contributory factor to the heavy casualties incurred. It was willingly accepted that, together, the physical protection and increased mobility conferred by APCs would not only reduce casualties

in themselves, but also enhance co-operation with tanks and raise the tempo at which operations could be conducted. So convincing were the arguments that all infantry, whether or not they were serving in tank divisions, became motor rifle troops, while the infantry division became a thing of the past and was replaced by the balanced all-arms motor rifle division.

The task of equipping the Army with APCs, therefore, was a formidable one, complicated by the fact that Soviet design teams had little or no experience in this field. However, the simple US M3 armoured half-track had been supplied to Russia during the war, though not in sufficient numbers to equip motor rifle units, and study of this and captured SdKfz 251 *Panzergrenadier* half-track APCs provided a starting point. In fact, the layout of the former and the angled plating of the latter were evident in the first Soviet APC, the BTR-152, which appeared in 1950, although the Russians chose to employ a 6 × 6 lorry chassis (the

An early production model BTR-152 APC on display with other equipment captured by South African troops in Angola *(South African Army)*.

ZIL-151 on the earliest models, followed by the improved ZIL-157) rather than a half-track system. The vehicle is powered by a front-mounted six-cylinder in-line petrol engine producing 110 hp at 2,800 rpm, weighs 9.1 tonnes (8.95 UK tons, 8.25 US tons) and has a maximum road speed of 75 km/h (47 mph). Frontal armour consists of 13.5 mm (0.5 in) plate laid back at 35 degrees and side armour 9 mm (0.35 in) plate at 7 degrees. Armoured doors and windshield shutters are provided for the commander and driver. A total of 17 infantrymen (a half-platoon) can be accommodated in the open-topped troop compartment, to which access is obtained through an armoured double door in the rear wall. In some versions the infantry benches are mounted transversely and in others down the sides. Each side of the troop compartment contains three firing ports with circular covers and there are two more in the rear wall. In action the infantry leave the vehicle either through the rear doors or over the side. Armament consists of a 7.62 mm machine-gun for which one forward and two side pintle mountings are provided in the troop compartment.

East German BTR-152V1 APC showing external pneumatic lines of the central tyre pressure control system.

BTR-152U command vehicle. A windowed superstructure has been added to the body of the basic APC to provide the necessary headroom.

66

The forward mounting has an elevation range from + 23.5 degrees to − 6 degrees and gives a traverse field of 45 degrees left and right of centre; occasionally a 12.7 mm heavy machine-gun is substituted for the lighter weapon on the forward mounting.

This, the basic BTR-152, is known in the West as the Model A and has been the subject of progressive modification. The BTR-152VI (Model B) is fitted with a central tyre pressure control system to improve cross-country performance and a forward-mounted winch; a simpler model, the BTR-152V2, is identical save that the winch is absent. The BTR-152V3 (Model C) is equipped with infrared driving lights and a winch, while the tyre pressure pneumatic lines, hitherto external, have been moved inboard. The final APC version, the BTR-152K (Model D) incorporates all these modifications as well as an overall armoured roof containing two hatches above the troop compartment. There is also a command version, the BTR-152U, which has been produced by adding a superstructure containing windows to the body of the vehicle and fitting the interior with the necessary communications equipment and map tables; this generally tows a trailer containing a charging generator for the radio batteries.

The simple layout of the BTR-152 has also rendered it very suitable as a weapons carrier and towing vehicle. It has been used as a carrier for the 82 mm and 120 mm mortars and as a tractor for the 160 mm mortar, the 85 mm and

100 mm anti-tank guns and the 122 mm howitzer. An air-defence version designated BTR-152A is armed with twin 14.5 mm heavy machine-guns in a manually controlled mounting which provides all-round traverse, elevation of + 80 degrees and depression of − 5 degrees. The Egyptian Army has fitted some of its BTR-152s with a quadruple 12.7 mm anti-aircraft mounting and the Palestine Liberation Organisation employed a twin 23 mm cannon mounting on the vehicle during the 1982 fighting against the Israelis in Lebanon.

The BTR-152 was first issued to the motor rifle regiments of tank divisions and by 1958 had become standard throughout the Soviet Army. However, like the BTR-40, it was something of an expedient design which took advantage of the ability to mass-produce from available assets and its lack of an amphibious capability was by then regarded as falling below operational requirements. Thereafter, it was steadily withdrawn from first line service in favour of purpose-built APCs, although the majority of Warsaw Pact armies still possess reserve stocks. The vehicle still remains active in the armies of the Soviet Union's clients. The People's Republic of China has produced a copy known as the Type 56 which has been exported to countries in receipt of Chinese military aid, notably Kampuchea, Tanzania and Vietnam.

In the tank division's motor rifle regiments the BTR-152 was replaced by the BTR-50P amphibious APC, which made its first public appearance in November 1957. This employs the chassis, engine, transmission and hydrojet water propulsion units of the PT-76 light tank and performs identically. The vehicle's crew consists of commander and driver, the former located in a small cupola equipped with three vision blocks at the left front of the hull. The first version was, like the BTR-152, a half-platoon APC capable of carrying up to 20 infantrymen in a central open-topped troop compartment in a manner reminiscent of the Sherman and Ram Kangaroos used by the British and Canadian armies in World War 2, entry and exit being obtained by climbing over the sides. The vehicle is equipped with a set of folding rear-mounted ramps which enable an anti-tank gun or other heavy weapon to be run aboard onto the engine deck for consolidation or a continued advance after a river crossing. Armament consists of a pintle-mounted 7.62 mm machine-gun with the usual arcs of fire. A slightly later production model, the BTR-50PA, dispensed with the loading ramps and is armed with a ring-mounted 14.5 mm heavy machine-gun above the cupola.

The majority of armies tend to favour section rather than half-platoon APCs, as the latter restrict tactical flexibility and their occupants sustain heavy casualties if they are penetrated. The Soviet Army seems to have concurred with these conclusions in about 1960 and this is reflected in the final APC version of this series, the BTR-50PK, which carries a rifle squad of up to 12 men and has an armoured roof incorporating rectangular access hatches. The vehicle is equipped with NBC protection and infrared driving lights; some models have one or two firing ports in the hull sides. A command version, the BTR-50PU, is distinguished by an additional cupola at the right front of the vehicle and up to five rod antennae. Another interesting developement is the MTB recovery and repair vehicle in which the troop compartment houses a mobile workshop under a raised armoured superstructure with NBC protection.

The highly developed Czech armaments industry has produced a much improved version of the BTR-50P series, designated the OT-62. This is powered by a six-cylinder supercharged diesel engine producing 300 hp at 1,800 rpm and has a maximum speed of 60 km/h (37.5 mph). External differences include an additional right-hand cupola in the manner

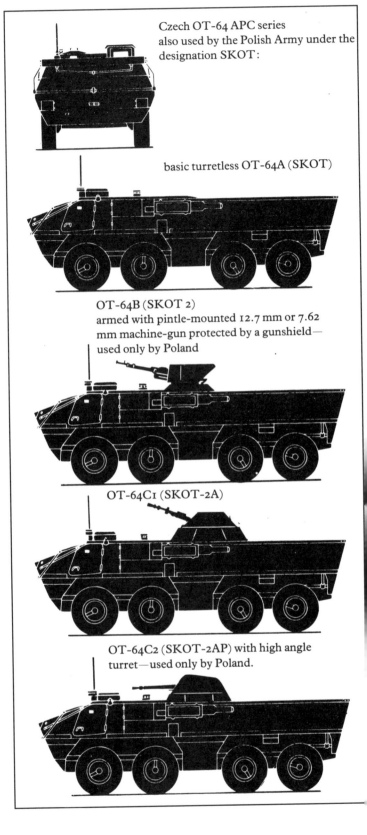

Czech OT-64 APC series also used by the Polish Army under the designation SKOT:

basic turretless OT-64A (SKOT)

OT-64B (SKOT 2) armed with pintle-mounted 12.7 mm or 7.62 mm machine-gun protected by a gunshield— used only by Poland

OT-64C1 (SKOT-2A)

OT-64C2 (SKOT-2AP) with high angle turret—used only by Poland.

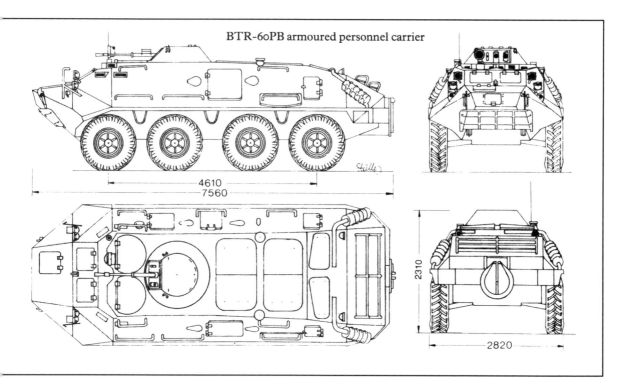

BTR-60PB armoured personnel carrier

4610
7560
2310
2820

T-55s and BTR-60P
APCs spearhead a
dismounted attack by a
motor rifle unit. In
severe weather the
troop compartment can
be protected by a canvas
cover. Note the open
weapon ports in the
sides of the nearest
vehicle.

+20 degrees and depression of −10 degrees. Mounted externally on the right of the turret is an 82 mm recoilless gun which fires HEAT ammunition. The OT-62C (Model 3) is fitted with a central, manually controlled turret mounting a 14.5 mm heavy machine-gun co-axially with a 7.62 mm machine-gun; this has all round traverse, an elevation of +89.5 degrees and depression of −4 degrees. The OT-62C is mainly employed by the Polish Army and Naval Infantry Corps, to whom it is known as the TOPAS-2AP. There are also command and recovery variants of the OT-62 series.

The BTR-50P is in service with Afghan-istan, Albania, Algeria, Congo, Cyprus, Fin-land, East Germany, Iran, North Korea, Rumania, Somalia, Syria, Vietnam and Yugo-slavia. However, the superior qualities of the OT-62 have made inroads into its potential export market and Russian and Czech vehicles operate in tandem in some armies including those of Angola, Egypt, India, Iraq, Libya and the Sudan. Other armies, including those of Czechoslovakia, Morocco and Poland, employ only the OT-62. In the Soviet Army the BTR-50P has now been withdrawn from active service with tank divisions, although reserve stocks are maintained.

of the BTR-50PU and doors in each side of the troop compartment, which has overhead pro-tection incorporating two rectangular hatches. Other standard features include an NBC sys-tem and an infrared driving light. The basic OT-62A or Model 1 is unarmed but the OT-62B (Model 1) has a small manually operated turret containing a 7.62 mm machine-gun fitted to the right-hand cupola; this gives all-round traverse, an elevation of

The shallow draft of the LCT enables this BTR-60PB to land almost dry-shod but the PT-76 on the right has its schnorkel erected and seems to have swum ashore. The ensign on the vehicles' trim vanes and hull sides indicates a Naval Infantry unit *(Novosti)*.

The contribution made by the BTR-50P series to the Egyptian Army's successful crossing of the Suez Canal on 6 October 1973 is well known, despite the unfavourable end to the operation involving the 130th Marine Brigade on the Great Bitter Lake. Less well known is a 'Trojan Horse' operation mounted by the Israeli Defence Force on 9 September 1969 in which four T-55 tanks and three BTR-50P APCs captured during the Six Day War were put ashore on Egyptian territory in the Gulf of Suez, destroying radar installations and inflicting several hundred casualties before re-embarking eight hours later.

The BTR-60P was first seen in 1961 and replaced the BTR-152 in the motor rifle regiments of the motor rifle divisions as well as equipping the Naval Infantry regiments. It is a 10.16-tonne (10-UK-ton, 9.2-US-ton) 8×8-wheeled amphibian and is believed to have been designed by the Dedkov bureau in Gorki, which was also responsible for the two BRDM scout cars. The open-topped hull of the vehicle is constructed from angled 7 mm (0.275 in) welded armour plate (9 mm (0.35 in) on the bow) and has a distinctive boat shape. A torsion bar suspension is employed with two shock absorbers each for the four leading wheels and a single shock absorber each for the remainder. Power is supplied by two six-cylinder in-line petrol engines each capable of producing 90 hp at 3,400 rpm, the right engine being coupled to the first and third axles and the left to the second and fourth. Assisted steering is provided for the four leading wheels. The vehicle is equipped with a central tyre-pressure control system and the tyres themselves are filled with foam to give a run-flat capability. The only preparation required for amphibious use is the erection of the trim vane on the bow and activation of a bilge pump. When afloat propulsion is by means of a single hydrojet which makes its exit through a port in the stern plate, giving a speed of 10 km/h (6.25 mph); a change of direction is effected by using the leading wheels as rudders. The BTR-60P has an excellent cross-

country performance and a maximum road speed of 80 km/h (50 mph).

The crew consists of commander and driver for whom windshields are provided; these can be protected by lowering hinged armoured shutters. Night movement aids include infrared headlights and a passive infrared periscope. An infrared searchlight which can be controlled from inside the vehicle is mounted above the commander's position. The BTR-60P was designed during the 1950s when half-platoon APCs were fashionable in the

Naval Infantry BTR-60PBs emerge from the water after swimming ashore. The spray pattern indicates that the leading vehicle has just disengaged its hydrojet and returned power to the wheels.

Upper view of BTR-70 showing exhaust details and hatches in the roof of the troop compartment.

BTR-70 APC. Although it is not easily discernible, a small access hatch is located in the lower hull, between the second and third wheels. The large exhaust ducts at the rear provide a prominent recognition feature.

Soviet Army, and up to 16 riflemen can be seated on transverse benches in the troop compartment, although in practice it is rare for more than 12 to be carried. Each side of the hull incorporates three covered firing ports and two access half-doors, but for the infantry entry and exit are normally obtained over the side. Armament consists of a forward pintle-mounted 12.7 mm heavy machine-gun or 7.62 mm machine-gun with provision for two further 7.62 mm weapons on either side of the hull.

The BTR–60PA entered service in the early 1960s and incorporated an overall armoured roof containing circular hatches for the commander and driver and two rectangular hatches above the troop compartment. This has enabled an NBC system to be fitted, the mushroom vent for which emerges from the roof of the troop compartment, on the right. The next development in the series is that in service today, the BTR-60PB, which is essentially the BTR-60PA fitted with the same manually controlled turret housing co-axial

Czechoslovakia and Poland have developed their own version of the BTR-60 series, designated OT-64 in Czech service and SKOT in Poland. These early turretless models, known as SKOT-1, are engaged in driver training (*Wojskowa Agencja Fotograficzna*).

14.5 mm and 7.62 mm machine-guns that are mounted on the BRDM-2 scout car; this version also introduced several periscopes into the roof of the forward compartment for the benefit of the commander and driver.

The last vehicle in the BTR-60 line entered service in 1978 and is actually designated BTR-70. This is very similar to the BTR-60PB but gives wider protection to the front suspension. The infantry section of six to nine riflemen sit back-to-back in the troop compartment, which contains three covered firing ports and a vision block in each side. Access to the troop compartment is by means of two small rectangular hatches in the roof and there are also two small doors in each side of the lower hull, between the second and third wheels. When the BTR-70 was first introduced it was thought in the West to be driven by two diesel engines as this would have extended the logical process begun with the issue of the BMP in which, in the tank divisions at least, tanks and APCs burn the same fuel. However, at the present time only one of the three motor rifle regiments in the motor rifle divisions is equipped with the BMP and as production of the BTR-60 and BTR-70 ended in 1982 the Soviet intention is clearly that the new vehicle merely complements the old, with which it will continue to serve in tandem until circumstances permit adjustment of this ratio. The BTR-70 is, in fact, powered by two six-cylinder petrol engines developing 115 hp each, and this additional power more than compensates for an increase in weight to 11.7 tonnes (11.5 UK tons, 10.6 US tons).

Comparatively few variants have been developed from this APC series, largely because of its narrow body. A command version of the BTR-60PA employs a canvas superstructure and a weaponless BTR-60PB is employed by forward ground controllers to direct air strikes.

The OT-64C2 (SKOT-2AP) is fitted with a turret capable of high-angle anti-aircraft fire (*Wojskowa Agencja Fotograficzna*).

72

There are also command, signals and recovery versions of the BTR-70, the last being turretless.

A modified version of the BTR-60PB is in service with the Rumanian Army. This is known as the TAB-72 and employs a high-angle turret with an elevation of +85 degrees in place of the standard turret in which elevation is limited to +30 degrees; this confers a definite advantage on a battlefield in which the helicopter in its various forms now plays a major role. The same vehicle, minus its turret, is employed as a mortar carrier. Rumania also manufactures the TAB-77 APC, which is essentially the BTR-70 powered by a single diesel unit and fitted with the same turret as the TAB-72.

Czechoslovakia and Poland have also developed their own version of the BTR-60 series, designated OT-64 in Czech service and SKOT in Poland. These are based on the chassis of the Tatra 813 8 × 8-wheeled lorry chassis and have a distinct gap between the second and third pairs of wheels. Both vehicles are powered by an air-cooled diesel engine developing 180 hp at 2,000 rpm and have a maximum road speed of 94.4 km/h (59 mph). When afloat they are driven by twin rear-mounted propellers. While retaining many of the characteristics of the enclosed models of the BTR-60, including an NBC system, infrared equipment and a central tyre-pressure control system, the layouts of the Czech OT-64 and Polish SKOT are radically different, the engines being housed between the driving and troop compartments. The crew consists of commander and driver and although it is possible to accommodate a half-platoon of riflemen it is rare for more than a section to be carried. The early models were turretless but the most common version in use today, the OT-64C1 (SKOT-2A), is fitted with the same turret as the BTR-60PB and BRDM-2, mounted centrally on an octagonal plinth the purpose of which is to permit more depression than would otherwise be obtainable, thereby reducing the area of dead ground surrounding the vehicle. The OT-64C2 (SKOT-2AP), used mainly by the Polish Army, is fitted with the same high-angle turret as the OT-62C tracked APC. Command and recovery versions of the OT-64 series have also been produced.

The BTR-60 series has been exported to Afghanistan, Algeria, Angola, Bulgaria, Chad, Congo, Cuba, Ethiopia, Finland, East Germany, Iran, Jibouti, North Korea, Mali, Mozambique, Nicaragua, Somalia, Vietnam, North and South Yemen, Yugoslavia and Zambia. In four more armies, those of India, Iraq, Libya and Syria, it serves in parallel with the OT-64. As well as equipping the Czech and Polish armies, the OT-64 serves as the principal wheeled APC of the Hungarian, Moroccan, Sudanese and Ugandan armies.

BTR-60s were employed by the Arab armies in their 1967 and 1973 wars with Israel and by the North Vietnamese Army in increasing numbers from 1972 onwards. They were also used in the Ogaden War between Ethiopia and Somalia and supplied to the Soviet-backed faction in Angola. In 1983 the communist forces on Grenada were found to be equipped with several. In Afghanistan the Mujahedin's ambush tactics have led to many of the Soviet Army's BTR-60s and BTR-70s being fitted with the AGS-17 automatic 30 mm grenade launcher.

Having entered the field of APC design late, the Soviet Army was nonetheless quick to appreciate that sooner or later like would inevitably meet like on the battlefield and that it would be the better-armed vehicle which would survive. Simultaneously, despite the relative success of the expedient APCs which had been introduced, the essential requirement remained for a high mobility, amphibious vehicle capable of keeping up with the new generation of MTBs in a rapid, deep-penetration offensive which might cover 65 to 100 km (40 to 60 miles) a day, some of which might have to be made over NBC-contaminated ground. These two demands were ingeniously satisfied by the Soviet designers in the BMP-1 IFV, which was developed during the early 1960s as a replacement for the BTR-50P. The vehicle made its first public appearance in November 1967 at a parade held in Moscow to celebrate the 50th anniversary of the Bolshevik coup, making a considerable initial impact on Western military observers as nothing comparable was then in service with their own armies.

The BMP-1 is a 13.7 tonne (13.5 UK ton, 12.4 US ton) vehicle which employs many of the same suspension components as the PT-76 light tank and is powered by an uprated model of the same engine, producing 300 hp at 2,000 rpm: this gives the vehicle a maximum road speed of 80 km/h (50 mph). The tracks are of the double-pin type, the top run being carried

The BMP-1 Infantry Fighting Vehicle (IFV) is armed with a 73 mm smooth-bore gun above which is a launching rail for a Sagger ATGW. The figures of the infantry section in the troop compartment emphasise the vehicle's cramped interior *(US Army)*.

Polish BMP-1s cross a training area. The photograph shows the weapon ports in the side of the troop compartment with individual periscopes above *(Wojskowa Agencja Fotograficzna)*.

by three return rollers. The driver is seated at the left front of the hull and is provided with three periscopes for use when closed down; a longer periscope can be substituted for these when the trim vane is erected for amphibious operations, enabling the driver to see over it. Immediately behind the driver is the commander who has a low, manually traversed cupola incorporating three periscopes and an infrared searchlight mounting. To the right of the driver and commander is the engine compartment.

Mounted centrally is a low, flat-topped one-man turret housing a 73 mm L/19 smoothbore gun and a co-axial 7.62 mm machine-gun with an elevation range from +33 degrees to -4 degrees. The gun is a low-recoil weapon system employing fin-stabilised HEAT ammunition similar to that fired by the SPG-9 recoilless anti-tank gun, although the primary propellant charge is different. The round itself contains a rocket motor which is automatically activated on leaving the muzzle, causing its velocity to increase from 440 to 700 m (1,444 to 2,297 ft) per second. It is effective up to 1,300 m (1,420 yd) but beyond 800 m (875 yd) its accuracy falls away rapidly and in cross winds its performance is erratic. An HE round is also employed for use against fixed positions and buildings. The weapon is served by an auto-loader and returns to an elevation of +3.5 degrees after each round is fired; gun elevation and turret traverse are electrically powered, with manual back-up. A total of 40 73 mm rounds can be stowed. For long range engagement of enemy armour, i.e. up to 3,000 m (3,282 yd), the BMP-1 is armed with five Sagger ATGWs, four stowed inboard and one on a launching rail mounted on the barrel of the 73 mm gun. Once one missile has been flown to its target another can be introduced on to the launcher through a narrow longitudinal hatch in the forward part of the turret roof. Despite this imaginative combination of gun and missile the BMP-1 has a large dead area in the left-frontal quadrant, extending from 295 degrees to 350 degrees, in which neither weapon system can be used. The reason for this is that if the gun is traversed into this arc the barrel would lie directly above the driver's and commander's hatches and so prevent their use in an emergency, as well as fouling the latter's searchlight, were it not for a safety device built into the turret ring which pushes it into full elevation. The gunner's sight has a

night-fighting capacity and the turret is equipped with four roof-mounted periscopes and a small white light or infrared searchlight.

Behind the turret is the troop compartment housing eight infantrymen seated back to back. Each rifleman has his own periscope in the roof and a firing port in the hull side. The roof contains four small hinged hatches which are normally locked open in a vertical position unless the vehicle is in contact with the enemy. Entry to and exit from the troop compartment is by means of double doors in the rear wall. These are hollow and contain part of the vehicle's diesel fuel supply, a feature which many regard as extremely dangerous; some sources suggest that on late production BMP-1s the double doors have been replaced by a powered ramp. Since the vehicle's height is only 1.92 m (6 ft) it can well be imagined that the troop compartment is unbearably crowded, but a low silhouette forms part of the Soviet design philosophy and the Russians attempt to solve this problem by recruiting only small men into their BMP regiments, as they do for their tank crews. Nonetheless, such cramped conditions inevitably reduce the rifleman's physical efficiency, especially if dismounted action is required at short notice, as does the inability of the ventilation system to clear cordite fumes from the compartment if weapons are in use.

The BMP-1 provides protection against small-arms fire and shell splinters, and the vehicle's frontal armour (lower hull front 19 mm (0.75 in) at 57 degrees, turret front 23 mm (0.9 in) at 42 degrees) is proof against heavy machine-guns. It is fitted with a pressurised NBC protection system and can produce a smokescreen by injecting diesel fuel into the hot exhaust. When afloat it is propelled and steered by its tracks at a maximum speed of 8 km/h (5 mph), a bilge pump being engaged for the duration of the crossing; because of the low freeboard a telescopic schnorkel has been installed directly behind the turret.

The standard BMP-1 equips the motor rifle regiment of the tank divisions and one of the three motor rifle regiments of the motor rifle divisions. A number of variants have been produced, of which the most numerous is the BMP-R reconnaissance vehicle which replaces the PT-76 light tank in reconnaissance units. This mounts the same armament as the BMP-1 but this is housed in a larger two-man turret. The troop compartment is smaller and has

A Hungarian BMP-1
company crosses the
Danube during Exercise
'Shield 79', involving
contingents from most
Warsaw Pact armies.
Because of the vehicle's
low freeboard when
afloat, a telescopic
schnorkel has been
fitted just behind the
turret (Novosti).

BMP-1 drivers under
instruction. The vehicle
is both low and fast,
providing a difficult
target in circumstances
other than a head-on
engagement, but in
other respects is poorly
protected (Wojskowa
Agencja Fotograficzna).

Czech and Hungarian motor riflemen compare notes during Exercise 'Shield 79'. The BMP-1 is marked on the hull with the white, red and blue Czech national roundel.

only two small hatches in its roof, suggesting that the only passengers carried are a two to four man scouting team. There are also command and communications versions designated respectively BMP-1U and BMP-1Ksh and a radar-equipped model is in service with self-propelled artillery units. A stretched version with seven roadwheels and a ramp replacing the rear doors has been supplied to Rumania, and possibly to Iran; this provision has probably been made to reduce congestion in the troop compartment. In Afghanistan Soviet BMP-1s have an AGS-17 automatic grenade launcher mounted on their turrets and a proportion have been fitted with a 30 mm cannon in place of the 73 mm gun, as this is obviously more useful in the type of warfare being waged. Side skirts have also been fitted to counter the Mujahedin's extensive use of captured heavy machine-guns and RPG-7 close-range anti-tank weapons.

In addition to serving with those armies already mentioned, the BMP-1 is also in service with Afghanistan, Algeria, Cuba, Czechoslovakia, Egypt, Ethiopia, Finland, East Germany, Hungary, India, Iraq, Libya,

North Korea, Poland, Syria and Yugoslavia. It first saw action during the 1973 Arab-Israeli war, large numbers being lost by the Syrians as a result of their being fed into the desperate tank battle on the Golan.

A complementary IFV, the BMP-2, began entering service in the Soviet Army during the late 1970s, although it was not seen by the public until November 1982. This employs the same chassis as the BMP-1 and has many of the same characteristics, but differs in a number of important respects. The most notable of these is the replacement of the 73 mm gun with a 30 mm cannon. Many similar kinetic energy weapon systems are employed by Western IFVs and light fighting vehicles to destroy their opposite numbers and it seems probable that the Russians reached the conclusion that quicker and more economic results can be obtained by this means than can be produced by the 73 mm gun; again, the ability of the latter's shaped-charge HEAT round to penetrate NATO MBTs has declined sharply with the introduction of Chobham armour, although the gun still has a role to play against infantry positions and buildings. The 30 mm

A busy scene on the vehicle part of a Hungarian motor rifle regiment. The national insignia on the turrets consists of a red star outlined in white with a white and green roundel in the centre.

T-62s and BMP-2s provide fire support for a dismounted winter attack. The BMP-2's main armament consists of a 30 mm cannon, plus a Spandrel ATGW mounted in a bracket on the turret roof. A battery of smoke grenade dischargers is fitted to each side of the turret.

cannon is housed in a two-man turret co-axially with a 7.62 mm machine-gun and has an elevation range from + 50 degrees to − 5 degrees; an infrared searchlight is located to the right of the gun mounting and is linked to it so that it has common elevation with the weapons. The fact that the 30 mm cannon mounting is seated higher in the turret than that of the 73 mm gun may well mean that the dead area which inhibited the BMP-1 has been eliminated as the barrel provides less of an obstacle to the driver's exit and so dispenses with the need for a safety elevation device, although this is unconfirmed. The BMP-2's armament is completed by a Spandrel AT-5 ATGW mounted in a bracket on the turret roof; this weapon has a maximum range of 4,000 m (4,376 yd).

The BMP-2's layout is also somewhat different from that of the BMP-1. The commander, who also leads the rifle squad during dismounted action, is positioned on the right of the turret and the gunner on the left. The commander has a low cupola incorporating three periscopes and an infrared searchlight mounting. The gunner has four periscopes, giving vision forward, to the left and to the rear. Both commander and gunner are equipped with day/night sights housed forward of their hatches. Six riflemen sit back to back in the troop compartment, which has two hatches in its roof, and a seventh, with his own hatch, is seated directly behind the driver in the position occupied by the commander in the BMP-1; each rifleman has his own periscope and weapon port. Entry to and exit from the troop compartment is made through the double doors in the rear.

Further distinctive features of the BMP-2 include short, hollow side-skirts which also give additional buoyancy, and a battery of six smoke grenade dischargers mounted three on each side of the turret. In other respects the vehicle differs little from the BMP-1 and although at 14.8 tonnes (14.6 UK tons, 13.45 US tons) it is over a tonne heavier the engine has been up-rated to 350 hp and its performance is very similar. For the moment the BMP-2 will not replace the older vehicle but will serve alongside it in the motor rifle companies, possibly on the basis of one or two BMP-2 platoons per company or one or two BMP-2s per platoon, as this will provide a tactical balance.

A light APC designated the BMD (*Broneveya Maschina Desantnaya* or Airborne Combat Vehicle) was designed for the Soviet Army's eight airborne divisions during the 1960s and began entering service in 1970, a specific requirement being that it could either be air-landed from a transport aircraft or para-dropped on a pallet. The vehicle is carried on a hydro-pneumatic suspension and its running gear consists of five road wheels, front idler, rear drive sprocket, two full and two half top return rollers. The suspension permits the hull of the vehicle to be raised and lowered. During para-dropping it is fully lowered to minimise impact damage; when raised it has a ground clearance of 45 cm (17.7 in). The BMP weighs 6.8 tonnes (6.7 UK tons, 6.2 US tons) and is powered by a rear-mounted 240 hp six-cylinder diesel engine giving a maximum road speed of 70 km/h (44 mph). It is also amphibious, being propelled when afloat by two hydro-jets housed in the lower stern plate; the usual trim vane is carried and the vehicle is equipped with an electric bilge pump with manual back-up.

The BMD is fitted with the same one-man turret as the BMP-1, mounting a 73 mm gun with Sagger ATGW launching rail above, a co-axial 7.62 mm machine-gun and an infrared searchlight. The driver is seated immediately in front of the turret on the vehicle's centre-line and although he has a pintle-mounted hatch that can be swung to the right, this is so narrow that it provides little more than a head-out facility, and then only with the gun at full elevation; three periscopes are fitted forward of the hatch for closed-down running. The commander and hull gunner are seated respectively to the left and right of the driver beneath

A BMD is released from its pallet after a large-scale parachute drop. The hydro-pneumatic suspension has been lowered to minimise damage and the return rollers can be seen in the gaps between the roadwheels.

Upper view of the BMD illustrating the severely cramped conditions in the troop compartment and the extreme difficulty experienced by the driver in using the forward hatch.

semi-circular hatches and it is probably through one of these that the driver enters and leaves the vehicle. The commander has one static and one movable periscope and the hull gunner, who fires two linked 7.62 mm machine-guns in fixed mountings at the lower corners of the glacis plate, has one movable periscope. The troop compartment is situated behind the turret, access being obtained through the roof, which opens to the front. Normally, four riflemen are carried here, although six appear on parade, the two additional members of the squad acting as vehicle commander and hull gunner in the field. Later production models incorporate two vision blocks and firing ports in each side of the troop compartment, but most vehicles lack these and are equipped with a single periscope in the roof. The BMD's armour is comparable to that of the BMP-1 and when fully closed down the crew are protected by an NBC overpressure system.

Comparatively few variants of the BMD have been produced. The 73 mm gun has been replaced by a 30 mm cannon on a proportion of vehicles and turretless versions with an extended hull and a sixth road wheel are employed as APCs, heavy weapons carriers and in the command role. As a result of experiences in Afghanistan, the armament of many BMDs has been supplemented by an AGS-17 automatic grenade launcher.

The BMD has been described as 'a quart contained in a pint pot' and although it is remarkable that so many characteristics have been combined in so small a vehicle, this has been achieved at the expense of the human engineering factor, since it is even more

As a result of the Mujahedin's ambush tactics, the majority of Soviet APCs and IFVs in Afghanistan are now armed with the AGS-17 automatic 30 mm grenade launcher which has an approximate range of 800 m (875 yd) and a 5 m (16 ft) burst radius. This example is shown on a ground mounting (South African Army).

The MT-LB multi-purpose tracked vehicle is based on the PT-76 light tank chassis and is generally thought of as an artillery tractor, but in Arctic conditions or swampland it is also used as an APC *(US Army)*.

cramped and overcrowded than the BMP and a long spell aboard is bound to have some effect on the physical efficiency of its occupants. The Soviet airborne division contains three rifle regiments each equipped with 109 BMDs, including ten command vehicles, nine turretless heavy weapons carriers and 90 basic APCs of which nine (i.e. one per company) are the 30 mm version; three further command vehicles are held by divisional headquarters, giving a total of 330.

During the Ogaden War of 1977–78 the Soviet Union gave an impressive demonstration of its airlift capability when it went to the aid of Ethiopia. Large numbers of BMDs, crewed by Russian, East German and Cuban advisers, spearheaded the counter-attack which drove the Somalis back agross the frontier, aided by the latter's shortage of anti-tank weapons. The BMDs of the 105th Guards Airborne Division played a critical part during the Soviet invasion of Afghanistan, simultaneously driving north and south from the airlanding zone at Bagram to secure, respectively, the strategically important Salang tunnel through which two motor rifle divisions had to pass, and key positions in and around Kabul, the capital. Since then, the 105th Airborne has remained the cutting edge of the Soviet effort

in Afghanistan, with the BMD as one of its principal tools.

Although not specifically designed as an APC, the MT-LB multi-purpose tracked vehicle is used as such in areas of particularly difficult going, including Arctic snowfields, Siberian swamps or central Asian deserts. The chassis of this 9.85 tonne (9.7 UK ton, 8.94 US ton) vehicle incorporates many of the same components as those on the PT-76 light tank. Layout is very simple and consists of a forward crew compartment, an engine compartment and a troop compartment at the rear.

The driver and vehicle commander sit respectively at the left and right front corners of the hull, the latter below a small manually controlled turret housing a 7.62 mm machine-gun, both being provided with windshields that can be closed by lowering hinged armoured shutters. However, the commander more usually occupies a hatch in the roof between the two positions: two roof-mounted periscopes are fitted immediately in front of this and three in front of the driver's hatch. The engine, a high-compression V-8 diesel producing 240 hp at 2,100 rpm, is located behind the driver on the left of the hull, leaving room for access between the crew and troop compartments. Eleven passengers can be car-

ried, seated down the sides and facing inwards. There are two hatches in the roof but entry and exit are usually made through two double doors in the rear wall, each of which is fitted with a vision block and weapon port. A further vision block and weapon port is contained in each side of the hull. Frontal armour is estimated at 14 mm (0.55 in) with 7 mm (0.275 in) elsewhere. An NBC system and infrared night fighting and driving aids are fitted as standard.

The MT-LB is equipped with the usual trim vane and bilge pump for amphibious use and is propelled by its tracks when afloat at a maximum speed of 5 km/h (3.1 mph). On hard roads the vehicle has a maximum speed of 61.5 km/h (38.44 mph). The normal track is 350 mm (13.78 in) wide, giving a ground pressure of 0.46 kg/cm² (6.54 psi). However, for use in snow, swampland or soft sand a special 565 mm (22.24 in) track can be fitted, reducing the ground pressure to 0.27 kg/cm² (3.84 psi), enabling the vehicle to operate in circumstances where the BMP and BMD, with respective ground pressures of 60 and 61 kg/cm² (853.5 and 867.7 psi), could not. This version is designated the MT-LBV.

The MT-LB series was designed in the 1960s as a replacement for a tracked artillery towing vehicle, the AT-P armoured tractor, and in divisions still equipped with towed guns it serves as a prime mover for the 100 mm anti-tank gun, the 122 mm howitzer and the 120 mm mortar. The series also includes a command vehicle (MT-LB-U), a recovery and repair vehicle (MTP-LB), an NBC reconnaissance vehicle (RKhM), an engineer vehicle, an armoured ambulance, several mountings for artillery fire control and locating radar sets, and a launch vehicle for the SA-13 (Gopher) low altitude Surface-to-Air Missile. An en-

larged version designated TT-LB, or ACRV (Artillery Command and Reconnaissance Vehicle) in the West, has been produced for the command group of self-propelled artillery regiments, one model being equipped as a command post and another with a fire control computer. The TT-LB is identified by its longer, deeper hull carried on a seven-wheel suspension, and by its low, central turret incorporating a 12.7 mm heavy machine-gun on an external anti-aircraft mounting.

Two motor rifle divisions based near Murmansk are equipped with the MT-LB as their standard APC and other similarly equipped formations are stationed in Siberia. As well as serving throughout the Soviet Army the MT-LB series has been supplied to Bulgaria, East Germany, Hungary, Poland and Yugoslavia. To date it has seen action only in Afghanistan.

7 · TANK DESTROYERS, ASSAULT GUNS AND SELF-PROPELLED ARTILLERY

During the Great Patriotic War the Soviet Army developed a number of simple assault guns and tank destroyers by installing various weapon systems in a fixed superstructure mounted on the front of tank chassis. This arrangement conferred two principal benefits, the first being that the roomier interior of the superstructure permitted a more powerful gun to be fitted than could be mounted in the tank turret carried by the parent chassis, and the second that this type of vehicle was quick and easy to build. Several of these vehicles, including the SU-85, SU-100 and ISU-122 tank destroyers and the ISU-152 assault howitzer, remained in service for many years after the war, until the advantage conferred by their weapons was eroded by steady improvements in gun and ammunition technology and their performance fell below that of the tanks they were intended to support.

The SU-85 and SU-100 were based on the chassis of the T-34. They were protected by 75 mm (2.95 in) frontal armour and manned by a crew of four, serving in the tank regiment's tank destroyer battalion in the mechanised infantry divisions, and in the tank destroyer units of mechanised infantry regiments. The SU-85 had been introduced while the T-34/76 was still the Soviet Army's principal medium tank and was armed with an 85 mm L/51.5 gun. This was the same weapon carried by the T-34/85, so that when the latter entered service the SU-85 offered no further advantage and by 1945 was already obsolete, although it remained on the active list a while longer before being withdrawn or exported; some of these vehicles are still held on the strength of the Korean and Vietnamese armies. The SU-100 was armed with the same 100 mm gun which was later fitted to the T-54/T-55 medium tank series, although in this case no fume extractor was fitted to the barrel. It was employed throughout the Warsaw Pact and was widely exported to the Soviet Union's clients, seeing action during the Korean War, with the Egyptian Army in 1956 and with the Egyptian and Syrian armies in 1967. It has long been withdrawn from active duty by the Soviet Army and most of its European allies, but reserve stocks are known to be held. On the other hand, the SU-100's robust simplicity has made it popular with its users and at the time of writing it is still listed as being in service with Albania, Algeria, Angola, China, Cuba, East

The ISU-152 assault howitzer was based on the IS heavy tank chassis. Because of the toll it took of Tigers and Elefants during the great tank battle of Kursk the vehicle was known in Soviet service as 'The Animal Killer' (IWM).

84

The ISU-122 tank destroyer was also based on the IS heavy tank chassis. The development of more powerful tank guns and better ammunition rendered the big-gun tank destroyer obsolete by the mid 1950s *(IWM)*.

The SU-100 tank destroyer was based on the T-34 chassis and was extensively used by the Egyptian and Syrian armies *(IWM)*.

Germany, Egypt, Iraq, North Korea, North Yemen, Rumania, Syria, Vietnam and Yugoslavia, though in the majority of cases it is doubtful whether it remains active in first line units. Stripped of their main armament, some SU-85s and SU-100s have been converted for use as command and recovery vehicles.

The ISU-122 tank destroyer and ISU-152 assault howitzer were based on the IS tank chassis. The former mounted a 122 mm L/43 gun with a double-baffle muzzle brake, or alternatively a 122 mm L/45 gun with a small counterweight on the muzzle, while the latter was armed with a 152 mm L/29 howitzer with a prominent muzzle brake. Both vehicles were protected by 120 mm (4.7 in) frontal armour and manned by a crew of five. They served in heavy tank destroyer/assault gun units, the task of which was to supplement the direct gunfire support available during a breakthrough battle, but apart from the ability to stow more ammunition, they offered little that the IS-3 and T-10 heavy tanks could not

provide and by the end of the 1950s were being phased out. A handful remain in service with Algeria, Syria and China.

Another vintage self-propelled mounting of which small numbers are still held by the armies of Albania, North Korea, Vietnam and Yugoslavia is the SU-76. This consists of an extended T-70 light tank chassis on which a 76.2 mm gun with double-baffle muzzle brake is housed in an open-topped compartment at the rear of the hull. The vehicle was a contemporary of the German Wasp and American M7 105 mm self-propelled howitzers but was less effective because of the lighter shell fired and was therefore obsolete long before the Great Patriotic War had ended, although it remained in service for some years after. While theoretically capable of indirect fire, and doubtless employed in this role, the task of the SU-76 was, more often than not, that of providing direct fire support against mechanised infantry objectives.

The chassis of the defunct T-70 light tank

The SU-76 self-propelled gun was based on the chassis of the obsolete T-70 light tank. This example, evidently a breakdown, was captured in Korea; clearly a struggle to start the engine has failed and attempts to tow the vehicle to safety have been abandoned (USAMHI).

Components of the T-70 light tank chassis are also used by the ASU-57 airborne tank destroyer, which was used operationally during the Ogaden War (Novosti).

also provided suspension components for the Soviet Army's first post-war self-propelled artillery weapon, the ASU-57 air-portable tank destroyer, which began entering service with the airborne divisions in the middle 1950s. The vehicle's running gear consists of four road wheels suspended from torsion bars, a front drive sprocket and two return rollers. Power is provided by a four-cylinder private car petrol engine providing 55 hp at 3,600 rpm, located in the right-front of the hull. The ASU-57 weighs 7.1 tonnes (7 UK tons, 6.45 US tons) and has a maximum road speed of 45 km/h (28 mph). The hull and open-topped crew compartment at the rear are constructed from 6 mm (0.24 in) aluminium armour plate which is proof only against small-arms fire. Armament consists of a 57 mm L/73 anti-tank gun, of which two versions have been employed, the first with a long slotted muzzle brake, later replaced by a double-baffle muzzle brake. The weapon enters the crew compartment just above the level of the hull and to the left of the vehicle's centre-line, its mounting giving an elevation of + 12 degrees, depression

of − 5 degrees and 8 degrees of traverse left and right of centre; when travelling the barrel is normally secured by a quick-release crutch.

Within the crew compartment the commander/gunner is seated on the left of the gun and the driver on the right with the loader behind him. The front plate of the compartment contains vision blocks for the commander and driver but is also hinged so that it can be folded forwards; lateral vision can be obtained through a single shutter in each side of the compartment. If necessary, three paratroopers can be carried at the rear. Thirty rounds of 57 mm ammunition are stowed vertically, including high explosive as well as armour-defeating rounds. One of the most remarkable features of the ASU-57 is its height, which is only 1.18 m (3ft 10 in) to the top of the crew compartment.

The ASU-57 can either be air-landed or para-dropped on a pallet. It was issued on the scale of three six-gun batteries per airborne rifle regiment, giving a divisional strength of 54. Nonetheless, while the design demonstrates considerable ingenuity in giving the

The ASU-85 airborne tank destroyer/assault gun employs the chassis and engine of the PT-76 light tank and began entering service during the early 1960s. This contingent forms part of the parade held in Moscow on 8 November 1967 to commemorate the 50th anniversary of the Bolshevik coup (*United Press International*).

lightly equipped airborne troops a mobile anti-tank-cum-assault gun capacity, the 57 mm gun—itself a veteran of the Great Patriotic War—is only capable of damaging modern tanks at very short range and the need for it disappeared with the arrival of the BMD APC. The ASU-57 has been supplied to Egypt, Vietnam and Yugoslavia, but has now been withdrawn to training use by the Soviet Army. A number were airlifted to Ethiopia and took part in the Ogaden War.

A larger air-portable tank destroyer/assault gun, the ASU-85, was developed for the airborne divisions during the late 1950s and was exhibited for the first time during the 1962 May Day parade in Moscow. The vehicle employs the same chassis components and engine as the PT-76 light tank, with an enclosed steel armour superstructure mounted centrally on the hull. The glacis consists of 40 mm (1.57 in) plate at 60 degrees and the sides of 15 mm (0.59 in) plate at 30 degrees. The ASU-85 weighs 15.75 tonnes (15.5 UK tons, 14.3 US tons) and has a maximum road speed of 44 km/h (27.3 mph). It is not amphibious but can ford to a depth of 1.1 m (3 ft 8 in) without preparation, a splash plate being fitted across the glacis.

Armament consists of an 85 mm L/53 gun fitted with a double-baffle muzzle brake and a fume extractor. This enters the superstructure somewhat to the left of the vehicle's centre line and is housed co-axially with a 7.62 mm machine-gun; an infrared searchlight is mounted on a flexible bracket directly above the mantlet and conforms to the movement of the gun. The gun itself has an elevation of +15 degrees, depression of −4 degrees and traverse of 6 degrees left and right of centre. Forty rounds of main armament ammunition can be stowed, including high explosive as well as armour-defeating rounds.

The four-man crew are all accommodated within the superstructure. The driver is seated on the right of the gun with a vision block and periscope to his front and a second vision block to his right. The commander is located behind him beneath a rectangular hatch in front of which is a periscope and a small infrared searchlight; later versions of the vehicle are fitted with a cupola with an anti-aircraft mounting for a 12.7 mm heavy machine-gun. The gunner and loader are seated on the left of the gun. It is probable that an NBC overpressure defence system is fitted.

Although the ASU-85 is normally air-landed, reports suggest that it is possible to para-drop the vehicle using a pallet fitted with retro-rockets which are fired during the final phase of the descent. The aircraft most usually employed is the Antonov An-12 Cub tactical transport, which has an airlift capacity of one ASU-85 or two ASU-57s. A divisional weapon, the ASU-85 was originally issued on the scale of 18 per airborne division, supplementing the ASU-57s as the situation demanded. Following the withdrawal of the latter, however, this scale has been increased to 31 guns, giving a battalion establishment of three ten-gun batteries and one gun in battalion headquarters. As the armour-defeating capability of the 85 mm gun has declined sharply since the ASU-85 was introduced, it is probably fair to suggest that the vehicle has more relevance today as an assault gun than as a tank destroyer, particularly so since the heavily armed BMD entered service. ASU-85s were air-landed at Prague in 1968 and again at Bagram air base in Afghanistan in 1979. Outside the Soviet Union, the vehicle is used only by East Germany.

With the exception of these tank destroyers and assault guns the Soviet Army relied on towed artillery weapons to support its armoured operations for almost 30 years after the end of the Great Patriotic War, a situation which Russian artillery officers must have found galling in view of NATO's continuous development of self-propelled guns and howitzers of all calibres. Indeed, during the 1950s and '60s it may well have seemed that this prestigious arm, once called Russia's 'God of War', was in a state of decline since it could offer little real improvement on the massive pre-planned bombardments which had characterised offensive operations in 1944 and 1945. At length a number of factors combined to make the introduction of self-propelled artillery a matter of necessity.

First, it was apparent that in the sort of fast-moving offensive for which the latest generation of tanks and APCs had been specifically designed, and which formed the cornerstone of Soviet strategy, there was simply no time available to prepare elaborate fire plans and stockpile the necessary ammunition. Secondly, neither NATO's artillery nor its air forces would tolerate hundreds of guns firing wheel to wheel in the old manner and casualties among unprotected gun crews would be critically

The 2S1 122 mm amphibious self-propelled howitzer is based on an extended MT-LB chassis. The hinged trim vane can be seen folded flat against the bow plate of the leading vehicle of this battery of Polish guns (*Wojskowa Agencja Fotograficzna*).

heavy; nor could the possibility of an NBC counter-strike against such an inviting target be discounted. Thirdly, although radio links form an essential part of their artillery battle, the Russians do not believe that the sort of flexible high level fire control system developed by Western armies will work for them because the net will be subjected to blanket electronic interference, a field in which NATO retains a lead. A solution to these problems was found in a complex system of decentralised artillery groups. These exist at army, divisional and regimental levels and keep pace with the offensive, each having a list of pre-designated targets to suppress and the ability, under local control, to engage opportunity targets, by direct gunfire if necessary. In view of the pace at which it is intended that operations should be conducted, this demands that artillery units possess an organic mobility comparable to the tanks and APCs they are supporting, and since the guns will be operating much closer to the forward edge of the battle than hitherto, it is also essential that they and their crews are protected as far as possible against conventional and NBC hazards.

During the early 1970s the Soviet Army introduced two self-propelled howitzers, the 122 mm 2S1 *Gvozdika* (Carnation) and the 152 mm 2S3 *Akatsiya* (Acacia), often referred to by their respective NATO designations of M-1974 and M-1973. The former is based on an extended MT-LB chassis with seven road-wheels, front drive sprocket and rear idler and is driven by the same V-8 240 hp diesel engine, located in the forward part of the hull with the driver to its left front. The 2S1 weighs 16.25 tonnes (16 UK tons, 14.75 US tons), has a maximum road speed of 55 km/h (34.5 mph) and is amphibious, being propelled by its tracks at 4.5 km/h (2.8 mph) when afloat. The vehicle has a pointed prow and a trim vane is fitted so that when swimming its forepart is not awash. In arctic conditions or soft going a 670 mm (26.4 in) wide track can be substituted for the 400 mm (15.75 in) wide standard track, thereby reducing the normal ground pressure of 0.5 kg/cm² (7.1 psi) by approximately one-third.

The flat-topped, D-shaped turret is located at the rear of the vehicle and can be rotated through 360 degrees. The commander and gunner are housed on the left and the loader on the right; the commander has a cupola with all-round traverse, incorporating three fixed periscopes and an infrared searchlight; the loader's

When afloat the 2S1 is propelled by its tracks at a speed of 4.5 km/h (2.8 mph). The trim vane pushes the water ahead of the vehicle and keeps its nose up.

Upper view of 2S1 122 mm self-propelled howitzer showing location of hatches. The weapon fires a 22 kg (48.5 lb) projectile to a range of 15,300 m (16,738 yd) and its rate of fire is five rounds per minute (US Army).

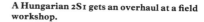

Dust swirls around the leaguer area of a 2S1 battery as crewmen hurry towards a briefing past a pair of TT-LB ACRVs.

fired are HE, HEAT, illuminating, smoke and chemical rounds. Maximum range with standard HE ammunition is 15,300 m (16,738 yd), but using a rocket-assisted projectile this can be increased to 21,900 m (23,959 yd). Up to five rounds per minute can be fired during a sustained programme. Forty rounds are stowed, the majority of which are HE.

At the present time the 2S1 is issued on the scale of one 18-gun battalion (three six-gun batteries) to the BMP-equipped motor rifle regiments of tank and motor rifle divisions, although this will probably change as more stocks become available to replace the large numbers of towed 122 mm howitzers which still form the bulk of the divisional artillery establishment. As the vehicle is air-portable, circumstances may also arise in which it can be employed in support of operations executed by airborne formations or the expanding Airborne Assault arm, which uses the helicopter for air-mobility operations. The 2S1 has seen active service in Afghanistan and is also used by the Algerian, Angolan, Czechoslovakian, Ethiopian, East German, Hungarian, Iraqi, Libyan, Polish, Syrian and Yugoslav armies.

The 2S3 152 mm self-propelled howitzer follows the general layout of the 2S1 but is based on an adaptation of the chassis developed for the SA-4 Ganef medium- to high-altitude Surface-to-Air Missile carrier-launcher, which is discussed in the next chapter. The 2S3 chassis, however, employs only six torsion bar suspended roadwheels, with hydraulic shock absorbers above the first, second and sixth wheel stations; there is a narrower gap between the third, four, fifth and sixth wheels than between the first, second and third, a necessary provision as so much of the vehicle's 23.37-tonne (23 UK-ton, 21.2 US-ton) weight is concentrated at the rear. The running gear is completed by a front drive sprocket and rear idler, plus two full and two half return rollers for the top run of the track. Power is provided by a V-12 520 hp diesel engine which can produce a maximum roadspeed of 55 km/h (34.5 mph). The 2S3 is not amphibious but can ford without preparation to a depth of 1.1 m (3 ft 4 in), a splash-plate being mounted transversely across the glacis.

hatch is located to his right and immediately forward of this is a swivel periscope; the gunner sits in front of and below the commander with the direct fire gunsight mounting protruding to the left of the gun. Additional access to the fighting compartment is obtained by means of a square door in the rear wall of the hull through which re-ammunitioning is also carried out. An NBC system is fitted.

The 2S1 is armed with a development of the 122 mm L/35.5 D-30 towed howitzer fitted with a double-baffle muzzle brake and a fume extractor. The gun control equipment is electrically powered with manual back-up, the elevation range being from + 70 degrees to − 3 degrees. A power rammer and semi-automatic breech ensure continuity of fire even at high angle. Included in the range of ammunition

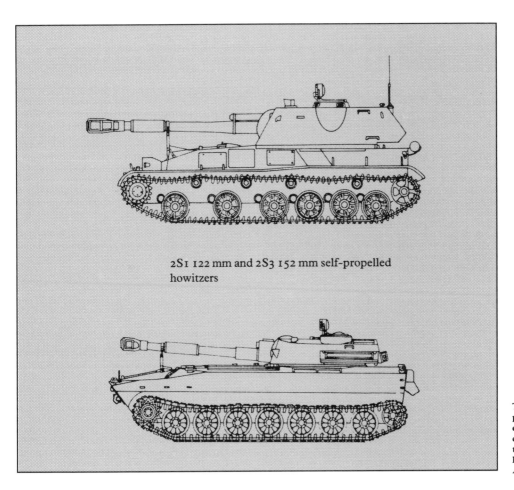

2S1 122 mm and 2S3 152 mm self-propelled howitzers

The 2S3 152 mm self-propelled howitzer employs a version of the chassis developed for the Ganef SAM carrier-launcher system (*US Army*).

Rear view of 2S3 showing the loader's hatch in the right wall of the turret and an access hatch in the stern plate of the hull. A shallow dozer blade is stowed beneath the turret overhang *(US Army)*.

The 2S3 is not amphibious but a splash-plate is welded across the glacis and it can ford without preparation to a depth of 1 m (3 ft 4 in). Dozer blade attachment points are just visible at the bottom of the bow plate *(US Army)*.

Upper view of 2S3 showing hatch details and dozer blade stowed across the rear of the hull *(US Army)*.

2S5 152 mm self-propelled gun photographed on a railway flat. The barrel is supported in the travelling position by a quick-release crutch and the recoil spade is lifted during transit.

At maximum elevation the 2S5 has a range of 27,000 m (29,538 yd), or 37,000 m (40,478 yd) with a rocket-assisted projectile. Note the position of the gun control equipment and gunlayer.

Crew positions conform to those of the 2S1 but the turret is much larger and has a rear overhang. The commander's cupola is partially set on to a circular projection in the turret wall and is similarly equipped to that of the smaller vehicle but is better designed and incorporates a mounting for a 7.62 mm machine-gun. Housed in the roof forward of the cupola is the gunner's periscopic sight. A hatch in the right side of the turret provides access for the loader and further access to the fighting compartment is obtained through a square hatch in the rear wall of the hull. The vehicle is fitted with an NBC defence system.

The 2S3 is armed with a modified version of the 152 mm L/37 D-20 howitzer, fitted with a prominent double-baffle muzzle brake behind which is a fume extractor; twin recoil cylinders protrude through the mantlet above the barrel. The weapon extends beyond the front of the vehicle and when travelling is normally secured by a quick-release crutch. Turret traverse and armament elevation controls are powered and have manual back-up, the elevation range being from +65 degrees to −3 degrees. A power rammer is almost certainly employed in conjunction with a semi-automatic breech. The ammunition fired in-cludes HE, HEAT, illuminating, smoke and chemical rounds, plus a two-kiloton tactical nuclear shell. Maximum range with standard HE ammunition is 18,500 (20,240 yd) but using a rocket-assisted projectile this can be increased to 24,000 m (26,256 yd). Two to three rounds per minute can be fired during a sustained programme. Forty-six rounds are stowed with HE predominating.

The vehicle is presently issued on the scale of 18 per tank and motor rifle division, equipping one three-battery battalion of the divisional artillery regiment, although this may be extended as its availability increases. It also serves in the army-level artillery brigades and what would become the front-level artillery divisions in the event of hostilities, replacing a proportion of towed 130 mm M-46 guns in both. The vehicle has been employed in Afghanistan and is also known to be in service with East Germany, Iraq and Libya.

Just as Soviet designers followed Western, and specifically American, practice in establishing the general configuration of the 2S1 and 2S3, this is also true of heavier self-propelled weapon systems which are known to have entered service in recent years, utilising the same chassis as the 2S3 with slight variations in

95

the wheel spacing. The best known is the 2S5, which is armed with a 152 mm gun installed on an unprotected mounting at the rear of the hull, with a recoil spade that is lowered prior to firing. No provision seems to exist for the crew, other than the driver, nor for ammunition, and it seems likely that both are transported in vehicles of the MT-LB/ACRV family. Maximum range with HE is 27,000 m (29,538 yd), or 37,000 (40,478 yd) with a rocket-assisted projectile; a nuclear shell can also be fired. As the layout of the 2S5 conforms to that of the US M107 175 mm self-propelled gun and M110 203 mm (8 in) self-propelled howitzer, the probability is that a recently introduced Soviet 203 mm self-propelled howitzer (designation as yet unknown) follows the same pattern. A 240 mm self-propelled mortar is also known to have entered service and is presently referred to as the M-1975 by NATO observers. This has a range of 12,700 (13,894 yd) and can fire HE or chemical rounds. These vehicles serve with the heavy regiments of artillery division and are only allocated operationally at the discretion of senior commanders.

8 · SELF-PROPELLED ANTI-AIRCRAFT WEAPON SYSTEMS

The *Blitzkrieg* technique demands complete command of the air above and in front of the advancing ground troops if the maximum possible benefit is to be gained from deep penetration operations into the enemy's hinterland. During the final two years of the Great Patriotic War the Soviets were able to achieve this, partly because of the growing strength of their tactical air arm, and partly because the bulk of the *Luftwaffe* had been withdrawn to counter the British and American bombing offensive against its homeland. In the post-World War 2 era, however, they are well aware that the NATO air forces are capable of inflicting critical losses on formations deployed in column of march and have taken immense pains to develop a fully mobile Air Defence arm which is present at every command level down to regiment and has the

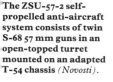

The ZSU-57-2 self-propelled anti-aircraft system consists of twin S-68 57 mm guns in an open-topped turret mounted on an adapted T-54 chassis (*Novosti*).

responsibility of severely curtailing the effectiveness of opposing aircraft, be they fixed-wing or helicopters. This employs both Anti-Aircraft Artillery (AAA) weapon systems for immediate local defence and Surface-to-Air Missiles (SAMs) for remoter targets, the effect of this integration being to provide an overall umbrella through low to medium and high altitudes. Thus, enemy aircraft attempting to fly below the SAMs effective height are immediately engaged by radar-controlled AAA. In recent years the importance of towed AAA weapons, particularly heavy guns, has declined following the introduction of more efficient self-propelled systems, low altitude SAMs and the shoulder-launched SA-7 missile with infrared homing device.

The Soviet Army's first purpose-built self-propelled AAA mounting, the ZSU-57-2, was

ZSU-57-2 turret traversed to the rear. The S-68 gun was designed to be fed from the left and because of this the right-hand gun has been turned through 180 degrees so that it can be fed from the right.

Business end of the ZSU-23-4 self-propelled anti-aircraft mounting showing the complex cooling and fume dispersal systems. The mounting itself is separated from the crew compartment by an armoured, gas- and fume-proof bulkhead (*Wojskowa Agencja Fotograficzna*).

developed during the early 1950s and was based on an adapted T-54 tank chassis with only four road wheels per side, the engine being mounted transversely at the rear. The vehicle weighs 28.5 tonnes (28 UK tons, 25.8 US tons), has a maximum road speed of 50 km/h (31.2 mph) and can ford without preparation to a depth of 1.4 m (4.6 ft), a splash plate being welded across the glacis; the driver is seated on the right and is provided with a night-vision periscope and an infrared driving light.

The ZSU-57-2's armament consists of twin S-68 57 mm L/71 light automatic anti-aircraft guns with small muzzle brakes housed in a large open-topped turret with rounded corners and inclined sides. The S-68 is actually a simplified version of the towed S-60 57 mm light anti-aircraft gun, but as the weapon was originally designed to be fed from the left the right-hand gun has been turned through 180 degrees so that it can be loaded from the right. Loading is by means of four-round clips inserted into magazines on either side of the twin mounting. Each weapon has a normal rate of fire of 70 rounds per minute, expended cases and clips being channelled automatically into a wire basket attached to the rear of the turret. Ammunition stowage consists of 264 rounds ready for use with a further 52 in reserve below the turret floor. When employed in the anti-aircraft role the S-68 has a vertical range of 8,800 m (28,880 ft), rising to 12,000 m (12,128 yd) when engaging ground targets. The turret has all-round traverse and the gun mounting gives an elevation range from −5 degrees to +85 degrees. Traverse and elevation/depression are powered, with respective speeds of 30 degrees per second and 20 degrees per second; manual controls are also fitted. The turret crew consists of the vehicle commander, gunner, fuze setter and two loaders, one on each side of the gun mounting.

The rapid acceleration in the speeds flown by high-performance jet aircraft rendered the ZSU-57-2 obsolete almost as soon as it was introduced, for it lacks radar guidance and relies on a comparatively slow clear weather optical-mechanical computer sight for its fire control predictions. Likewise, the obvious impracticability of installing an NBC defence system has long rendered it unsuitable for use against NATO armies in Europe. The vehicle served with the anti-aircraft batteries of tank regiments but as far as the Warsaw Pact armies are concerned has now been relegated to reserve and training uses, although it remains on the strength of several armies around the world, including those of Algeria, Angola, Cuba, Egypt, Ethiopia, Iran, Iraq, North Korea, Syria, Vietnam and Yugoslavia. It saw active service during the Arab-Israeli and Vietnam wars, but the results it produced were disappointing.

The ZSU-57-2's replacement is the ZSU-23-4 self-propelled AAA mounting, which was developed during the early 1960s and made its first public appearance in 1965. This vehicle is based on the PT-76 light tank chassis, weighs 19.3 tonnes (19 UK tons, 17.5 US tons), has a maximum road speed of 44 km/h (27.5 mph), and can ford without preparation to a depth of 1.07 m (3.5 ft). The driver is seated to left of the centre line behind a hinged access hatch set into the glacis in a manner reminiscent of the T-34.

Armament consists of four belt-fed 23 mm L/81 cannon in a quadruple mounting which occupies the forward part of a low, square turret, each weapon being theoretically capable of an output of 1,000 rounds per minute, although in practice this rate is restricted to 200 rounds per minute, fired in short bursts; 2,000 rounds can be stowed inboard. When employed against aircraft the cannon have an effective ceiling of 2,500 m (8,205 ft), and against ground targets a maximum range of 7,000 m (7,658 yd). The turret has all-round traverse and the weapon system can be elevated from −4 degrees to +85 degrees. Both the vehicle commander and gunner can engage the power traverse mechanism, which turns the turret at a speed of 45 degrees per

Although each barrel is theoretically capable of an output of 1,000 rounds per minute, in practice this is restricted to approximately 200 rounds per minute, fired in short bursts. Even so, the volume of exhausted propellant fumes is considerable.

second; elevation is also powered and manual back-up is provided for both dimensions. Access to the guns is gained through two large hatches on either side of the turret roof, but the weapons are separated from the turret crew by an armoured, gas- and fume-proof bulkhead.

The crew compartment of the turret houses the vehicle commander, search radar operator/gunner, range operator, radar sets, fire control computer and stabilisers. The radar system, codenamed Gun Dish in the West, employs a circular antenna mounted on the rear of the turret. The data obtained enables approaching aircraft to be identified as friendly or hostile, provides target tracking parameters and is used in the electronic calculation of the range and angles of engagement. A radar-controlled engagement takes between 20–30 seconds from the time the target is acquired until the guns open fire. Alternatively, a quicker response is obtained if only the range is taken from the radar and the engagement is conducted using optical sights, but clearly this sacrifices a degree of accuracy. Finally, in situations where electronic counter-measures (ECM) inhibit the use of the radar it is possible to engage

using only the optical sights. The vehicle normally opens fire from a stationary position but can engage on the move although this severely degrades accuracy, despite the use of stabilisers. Early models tended to suffer from runaway guns, a phenomenon induced by overheating which causes rounds to 'cook-off' in the breech until the belts have been expended. This made the ZSU-23-4 an unpopular neighbour with the troops it was supporting, particularly if the weapon system was still tracking low-flying aircraft, and the tendency has been to allow the vehicle plenty of room in which to operate. However, the cooling system has been the subject of constant modification and the probability is that the fault has now been cured. Other features of the vehicle include an NBC system, infrared night driving aids and an inertial navigation system.

The ZSU-23-4 is issued on the scale of one four-vehicle platoon to the anti-aircraft batteries of tank and motor rifle regiments, giving a total of 16 per division. Eight of these vehicles also form part of the battalion establishment of the SAM brigades which operate at front and army level. The ZSU-23-4 saw action in Indo-

Numerous minor variants of the ZSU-23- have been produced. This version, designated ZSU-23-4M, incorporates additional stowage capacity and improved electronic equipment *(US Army)*.

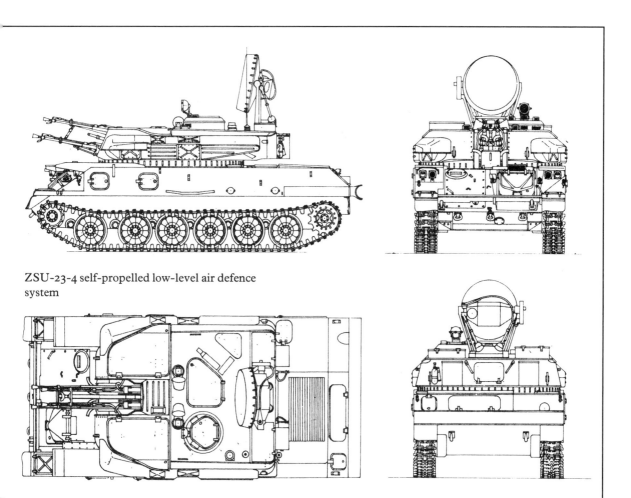

ZSU-23-4 self-propelled low-level air defence system

China and during the 1973 Arab-Israeli war; in the latter conflict it provided a formidable defence against low-level strafing attacks made below the effective SAM ceiling and was credited with 30 of the 80 Israeli aircraft destroyed in the first three days' fighting. The vehicle is in service throughout the Warsaw Pact and has been exported to the majority of the Soviet Union's clients in the Middle East, Africa and Asia.

Although the ZSU-23-4 is a proven weapon system that will remain operational for many years to come, the Soviet Army is known to have developed an alternative armament which can be substituted for the quadruple 23 mm cannon. This consists of six 30 mm cannon, the barrels of which rotate around a central axis on the Gatling principle and while at the time of writing it has yet to be seen in public it is understood to have been designated ZSU-30-6.

The Air Defence Troops' tactical and operational level SAM units have been given a mobility comparable to the self-propelled AAA vehicles they complement by the development of a series of carrier-launch vehicles. That used by the SA-4 *Krug* (NATO designation Ganef) medium-to-high altitude missile system was purpose-built for the task and employs a torsion bar suspension with seven medium-sized road wheels, front drive sprocket, rear idler, two full and two half return rollers. The vehicle weighs 25.4 tonnes (25 UK tons, 23 US tons), is powered by a 600 hp diesel engine and has a maximum road speed of 50 km/h (31.28 mph). The launcher arms are mounted on a turntable with all-round traverse and support two missiles, each with a launch weight of 2,500 kg (5,512 lb). When travelling they are lowered to the horizontal with the missiles pointing forward and secured by a large folding clamp attached to

SA-4 Ganef surface-to-air missile and carrier-launch vehicle.

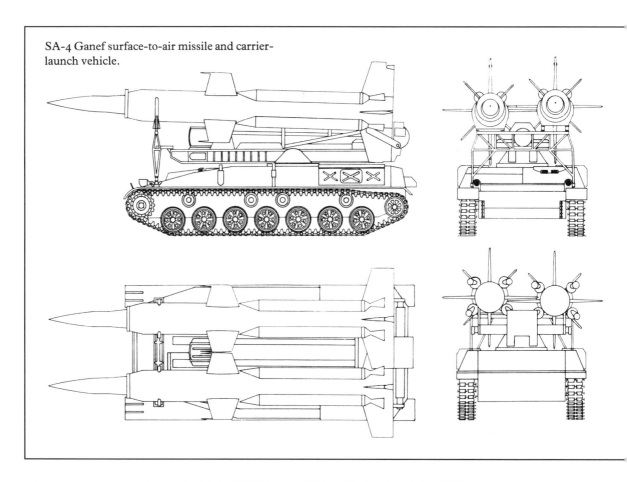

The SA-4 Ganef medium-to-high altitude SAM system employs a carrier-launch vehicle that was purpose-built for the task. The Soviet designation of the SA-4 is *Krug* (UPI).

The hull and chassis of the SA-6 Gainful (*Kub*) low-to-medium altitude SAM carrier-launch vehicle is similar to that of the ZSU-23-4 (*Novosti*).

During transit Gainful SAMs are normally carried pointing to the rear. The entire system is air-portable (*AP*).

the front of the vehicle. The SA-4 is employed in brigade strength, each brigade consisting of headquarters, three SAM battalions each of three four-launcher batteries, eight ZSU-23-4s, organic radar and re-load vehicles, plus a radar battalion. Each army, whether tank or combined arms, is assigned one SA-4 brigade, and each front two. The missile first appeared in 1964 and both it and its radar support systems are vulnerable to ECM; it is reputedly being replaced by the more recently developed SA-12 (Gladiator), which has a longer range and also employs a tracked carrier.

The SA-6 *Kub* (Gainful) low-to-medium altitude missile system employs a hull and chassis similar to that of the ZSU-23-4 and is air-portable in an An-22 or Il-76 aircraft. The missile has a launch weight of 550 kg (1,213 lb) and three are carried on a turntable mounting, normally traversed to the rear when travelling. The SA-6 equips the Air Defence Regiment of tank and motor rifle divisions, which consists of headquarters and regimental radar unit and five SAM batteries; at war establishment each battery contains six launch vehicles, organic radar vehicle and two reload vehicles with six reserve missiles. Unlike the SA-4, which is used only by the Soviet, Bulgarian, Czechoslovakian and East German armies, the SA-6 equips the entire Warsaw Pact and is also in service with Algeria, Cuba, Egypt, India, Iraq, Kuwait, Libya, Mozambique, Syria, Tanzania, Vietnam, North Yemen and Yugoslavia. It first saw action with the Egyptian and Syrian armies during the 1973 Middle East war in the opening phases of which it was largely responsible for forcing Israeli aircraft to fly low into the teeth of AAA fire. As the war progressed, however, the IAF developed countermeasures, including a steep dive towards the climbing missile and the release of chaff bundles that were acquired by its terminal homing radar, and its effectiveness declined; subsequent analysis suggests that overall one kill was scored for every 55 SA-6s fired. It has been further used by the Syrians in the 1981–82 fighting in the Lebanon, by Iraq in her war with Iran, by Egypt and Libya in their border war of 1977, and was almost certainly launched against American aircraft during their anti-terrorist strikes against targets in Tripoli and Benghazi in 1986.

The SA-6 was introduced some 20 years ago and in many divisional air defence regiments

has been at least partially replaced by the SA-8 *Romb* (Gecko) low-altitude missile system, which first appeared in 1975. This has been designed to fill the altitude gap which existed between the shoulder-launched SA-7 and the SA-6 and employs a wheeled carrier launch vehicle based on the chassis of the ZIL-167 heavy lorry. The vehicle has the same airportable characteristics as the SA-6 and is amphibious, being propelled when afloat by two hydrojets in the rear of the hull. The SA-8 carrier mounts four forward-pointing missiles but on recently introduced models the number has been increased to six, this version being designated SA-8b. Surveillance and guidance radar sets are fitted directly forward of the launching arms and an optical guidance system has been installed for use when the radars are inoperable because of ECM. At present the SA-8 is in service with the Soviet, Indian, Iraqi, Jordanian and Syrian armies. It has seen active service in the Lebanon and Iraq.

Another low altitude missile system is the SA-9 *Strela-1* (Gaskin), four of which complement the ZSU-23-4s in the air defence batteries of tank and motor rifle regiments. Introduced in 1968, the SA-9 employs the BRDM-2 scout car as a carrier-launch vehicle, the turret being replaced by a narrow turntable superstructure with four launching boxes attached; these are elevated for use but are normally lowered during transit. Four

The SA-8 Gecko (*Romb*) low-altitude SAM system employs a wheeled carrier-launcher on the chassis of the ZIL-167 heavy lorry.

A more recently
introduced version of
the Gecko air defence
system is designated
SA-8B, the number of
missiles carried being
increased from four to
six (*Novosti*).

Side view of SA-9
Gaskin (*Strela-1*) SAM
launcher based on the
BRDM-2 scout car,
showing details of the
retractable launching
arm. This example was
captured in Angola
(*South African Army*).

An SA-9 heat-seeking
SAM streaks away from
its launcher. Four
reload missiles can be
carried on folding racks
mounted on either side
of the vehicle's hull
(*Wojskowa Agencja
Fotograficzna*).

The SA-9 is being
replaced by the SA-13
Gopher (*Strela-10*)
SAM system which
employs a similar
launching arm but is
carried aboard a variant
of the MT-LB series.
The air-defence battery
on the left is armed with
SA-6 Gainful SAMs
(*Novosti*).

reload missiles can be carried on folding racks mounted on either side of the hull. The missile itself has a launch weight of 50 kg (110 lb) and its 4 kg (8.8 lb) warhead is fitted with an infrared heat-seeking device which can be decoyed in a number of ways including the emission of flares by target aircraft. The system has been employed in the Lebanon by Syria, by Iraq in the Gulf War and against South African aircraft carrying out cross-border strikes into Angola. It is also in service with Algeria, Czechoslovakia, East Germany, Egypt, Hungary, India, Libya, Poland, Vietnam and Yugoslavia.

The SA-9 is presently being replaced by the SA-13 *Strela-10* (Gopher) low-altitude missile system. This is based on a variant of the amphibious MT-LB general purpose tracked vehicle and is equipped with the same type of launcher as the SA-9. The missile itself has a 6 kg (13.2 lb) warhead fitted with a refined heat-seeking homing device that enables it to filter out the influence of decoy flares. Four missiles are carried in the launch boxes and 16 reloads are housed within the hull.

The latest generation of surface-to-air missiles includes the self-propelled SA-11 low-to-medium altitude system which employs the ZSU-23-4 chassis with four missiles carried on a turntable mounting. The SA-11 complements and will eventually replace the ageing SA-6 and is presently issued on the scale of at least one to each SA-6 battery, although this proportion will rise as more become available. The missile is known to have radar guidance and its speed of Mach 3 is twice that of the SA-6. The SA-11 system is present with the Group of Soviet Forces Germany (GSFG) and has also been supplied to Syria.

Tactical surface-to-surface missile carriers and assault engineer equipment

In the late 1950s the Soviet Army began introducing a series of short-range self-propelled battlefield support surface-to-surface missile systems for use against known nuclear sites, headquarters, airfields and critical centres of resistance, capable of delivering a nuclear, chemical or high explosive warhead. These received the collective NATO code-name of FROG (Free Rocket Over Ground), the missiles being unguided but spin-stabilised in flight by cruciform fins. FROGs 2, 3, 4 and 5 are air-portable by an An-22 transport aircraft and all employ the chassis of the PT-76 light tank as a carrier-launch vehicle. The FROG-2 can deliver a 545 kg (1,200 lb) warhead to a maximum range of 19 km (12 miles), while FROGs 3, 4 and 5 have a 454 kg (1,000 lb) warhead and respective maximum ranges of 45 km (28 miles), 50 km (32 miles) and 35 km (21.7 miles). The most recently introduced of these weapon systems, the FROG-7, entered service in 1965 and employs an eight-wheeled ZIL-135 transporter as a carrier-launch ve-

hicle; it can deliver a 450 kg (990 lb) warhead to a range of 60 km (37 miles). Each tank and motor rifle division has its own Heavy Rocket Launcher Battalion currently equipped in the former case with four FROG-7s and in the latter with four FROG-4s or FROG-7s. FROG systems have been supplied to the Warsaw Pact armies but are little used elsewhere. During the 1973 Middle East war both Egypt and Syria launched FROGs against Israeli targets but the results produced were very poor, particularly as regards accuracy.

Medium-range self-propelled surface-to-surface missile systems are employed at front and army level. The first of these to enter service, the Scud A, used the chassis of the obsolete IS-3 heavy tank as a carrier launcher. The missile had a maximum range of 180 km (110 miles), delivered a 680 kg (1,500 lb) warhead and was equipped with radio command guidance. This was soon replaced by the Scud B, which also used the IS-3 chassis initially but subsequently employed the eight-

The IS-3 heavy tank chassis was adapted as a carrier-erector for the Scud medium-range surface-to-surface missile systems. The missiles shown here as Scud-Bs, known in Soviet service as the *Luna-M* *(Novosti)*.

The IS-3 chassis was also used as the basis of a carrier-erector for the enormous Scrooge surface-to-surface missile system, which is manned by the Soviet Army's Strategic Rocket Forces *(AP)*.

wheeled MAZ-543 transporter-erector-launcher. The missile is fitted with an inertial guidance system and can deliver an 860 kg (1,986 lb) warhead to a distance of 280 km (170 miles). The Scaleboard system entered service in 1969 and this, too, uses the MAZ-543 transporter. It has a maximum range of 800 km (500 miles) but no details of its payload weight

are available. There is little demand for these vehicles outside the Warsaw Pact although the Scud B has been supplied to Egypt, Syria, Iraq and Libya; in 1973 several of these missiles were fired by the Egyptians at the Israeli bridgehead across the Suez Canal and its approaches, but again the results were disappointing.

A T-55 company crosses a PMP pontoon bridge during Exercise 'Dniepr' (1967). Vehicle intervals are carefully regulated by the movement control staff *(Novosti)*.

On land the GSP self-propelled raft system employs a variant of the amphibious PT-76 chassis with a pontoon carried in an inverted position above the vehicle. When afloat, two such units constitute the complete raft, which takes less than five minutes to assemble.

The GSP raft has a 51-tonne capacity and is driven by four propellers at a maximum speed of 8 km/h (5 mph).

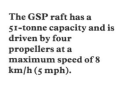

T-55 driver revs up as he prepares to take his vehicle ashore over the raft's submerged exit ramps. The raft's engines remain running to counteract the tank's reverse thrust.

SKOT APCs of a Polish motor rifle unit come ashore from a large vehicle ferry (*Wojskowa Agencja Fotograficzna*).

The inaccuracy of these weapon systems, coupled with the long period of preparation required before they can be activated and the fact that quicker, more reliable means of delivery do exist, provides food for thought as to whether they still fit into the contemporary pattern of Soviet offensive strategy and gives rise to speculation as to how long their exponents can justify their place in the divisional order of battle. Although only remotely relevant to the study of Russian armour, it is worth mentioning that the Soviet Army's Strategic Rocket Forces also employ developments of the IS-3 chassis as carrier-erector-launchers for their enormous Scamp/Scapegoat and Scrooge surface-to-surface missile systems.

The assault engineering aspects of offensive warfare have received intense study by the Soviet Army, especially the problems encountered in crossing water obstacles such as rivers and canals, and ample engineer assets are present at every level from front down to regiment, lavishly equipped to deal with every contingency. Each front possesses two or more assault engineer regiments, two pontoon bridge regiments and up to three assault crossing battalions. Each army has one assault engineer regiment, one pontoon bridge regiment and up to two assault crossing battalions. Each tank and motor rifle division has its own

engineer battalion which includes a mine warfare company with minelaying and mine-clearing equipment; an engineer company with obstacle clearing, earth moving, field fortification and mobile bridging equipment; a pontoon bridge company and an assault crossing company. Each tank and motor rifle regiment has its own engineer company including a bridging platoon, a mine warfare platoon and a demolition and obstacle clearing platoon. Thus, according to the requirements of the master plan, regimental engineers can be reinforced with divisional assets, divisional engineers with army assets and army engineers with front assets, the primary object being to maintain the momentum of the advance despite natural and man-made obstacles in its path.

Some idea of the Soviet Army's ability to take water obstacles in its stride was gained during the successful Egyptian crossing of the Suez Canal in October 1973. While the eastern bank was being stormed by the assault wave the Egyptians' Soviet-built pontoon bridging trains were moving forward to the crossing sites and once these had been secured and prepared the bridges themselves were quickly put in. These included the 61 tonne (60 UK ton, 55 US ton) PMP, the 51 tonne (50 UK ton, 46 US ton) TPP and the 25.4 tonne (25

The BAV amphibious lorry bears more than a passing resemblance to the US Army's DUKW of World War 2 and is driven by a single propeller. The vehicle is ferrying a 76.2 mm field gun and its crew (US Army).

MTU-55 scissors bridgelayer aboard a GSP raft. The MTU-55 is actually Czech-designed and is in service with several Warsaw Pact armies. It has a 51 tonne capacity and a 16 m (17.5 yd) span.

UK ton, 23 US ton) LPP systems, all of which are carried on trucks. Being of sectional construction, they could be repaired rapidly with spare pontoons if damaged by air attack or artillery, but so thorough was the Egyptian planning that a dummy bridge was also installed to absorb some of the Israeli response. Another system employed was the 51-tonne GSP sectional motorised raft, which is transported on a tracked chassis prior to launching. Such was the success of the operation that between seven and ten hours after the initial assault had gone in armour and heavy weapons began streaming across the canal into the bridgeheads, assisting in the defeat of weak and unco-ordinated Israeli counter-attacks. Nonetheless, however impressive this achievement might have been in its planning and execution, the crossing itself was made in ideal circumstances with all assets in hand and against very light opposition, conditions which are unlikely to repeat themselves.

For less formidable water obstacles the Soviet Army employs the truck-launched TMM sectional trestle bridge which has a capacity of 61 tonnes. Spans incorporate trestle legs and are transported folded, opening as they are launched over the rear of the carrying vehicle. Once the launch has passed the vertical stage the trestle legs drop and find support on the river bed. This system can be used over stretches of water not exceeding 3 m (9.8 ft) in depth and is quick and easy to assemble; a four-span 40 m (43.76 yd) TMM bridge, for example, takes an hour to install by day and slightly longer by night.

Small streams and demolition craters in roads can be crossed using armoured bridge-layers from divisional or regimental resources. These employ the T-54 or T-55 tank chassis and launch their bridges hydraulically over the bows. The oldest is the MTU which lays a straight cantilever bridge with a 51-tonne capacity capable of spanning an 11 m (12 yd) gap. A more recent development is the MTU-20 which also has a 51-tonne capacity but the ability to span an 18 m (19.7 yd) gap, the bridge again being of the straight cantilever type with the entry and exit ramps folded

The BAT/M dozer is also fitted with a 2,000 kg (4,410 lb) jib crane. The vehicle is based on the AT/T artillery tractor.

(Left) The BTU-55 tank dozer blade can be attached to a T-54, T-55 or T-62 main battle tank and can move up to 250 cu m (8,829 cu ft) of earth an hour.

(Right) The BTM rotary digger can excavate 500 m (547 yd) of 1.6 m (5.25 ft) deep trench in an hour and is also fitted with a dozer blade.

inwards during transit. In service with several Warsaw Pact armies, including that of the Soviet Union, is a Czech-designed scissors bridgelayer with a 51-tonne capacity capable of spanning a 16 m (17.5 yd) gap. This vehicle, designated MTU-55 in Soviet service, can schnorkel its way across river beds and is equipped with night vision devices and an NBC system.

For obstacle-clearing the Soviets use the IMR combat engineer vehicle, based on the T-54/T-55 tank chassis. This is equipped with a dozer blade and digging equipment but its principal tool consists of a hydraulically operated flexible arm ending in a mechanical claw capable of lifting trees and heavy objects. The vehicle can operate under fire and is fitted with night vision devices and NBC protection. Another engineer vehicle capable of a variety of tasks is the BAT dozer, based on the AT-T

(Right) **After being sprayed with decontaminant, vehicles are scrubbed down. The BRDM-2rkh NBC reconnaissance scout car is identified by the rack of lane marker pennant poles mounted on its rear.**

(Above) **T-54-T armoured recovery vehicle with ground spade. A training schnorkel tube is stowed across the top of the hull.**

(Left) **BRDM-2 scout cars are sprayed with NBC decontamination fluid by the high-pressure TMS-65 system. The TMS-65 is mounted on a URAL-375 tanker and can be adapted as a smoke generator.**

A BMP company replenishes its fuel supply at a multi-point bowser.

A Hungarian patrol dismounts from its scout car for a reconnaissance on foot. The men are wearing NBC suits, the hoods of which can be drawn tight around a gas mask using draw strings.

tracked artillery tractor. This can move up to 400 cu m (14,126 cu ft) of earth in an hour and is often employed in the construction of cross-country routes, for example to and from bridge launching sites or around uncleared obstacles, working at a speed of 9.5 km/h (6 mph) in clear terrain or up to 6.4 km/h (4 mph) in woodland. In addition the BAT is fitted with a 2,000 kg (4,410 lb) capacity jib crane. For local use the T-54, T-55 and T-62 tanks can also be fitted with a dozer blade, enabling them to move up to 250 cu m (8,829 cu ft) of earth an hour.

The third major element of assault engineering is mine warfare and in this area the Soviet Army has developed a variety of weapons for both offensive and defensive use. Several mine-clearing devices employ explosive charges contained in tubes or flexible hoses which are either pushed into or rocket-launched across a minefield and then detonated, clearing a path forwards. One such method consists of two rockets of the Swatter type mounted on the rear of a tank or BTR-50PK tracked engineer APC which, when fired, haul a 170 m (186 yd) explosive hose forward for firing by remote control. A somewhat slower means of breaching a minebelt is provided by the PT-54/55 mineroller system, consisting of two independent sets of rollers attached to the front of a tank in line with the tracks. As these are pushed forward their weight explodes the mines below, clearing two paths each slightly wider than the width of the vehicle tracks. The rollers take approximately 15 minutes to fit and can survive the explosion of up to ten anti-tank mines. A modern version of the same system, the KMT-4/5, employs three sets of rollers and a plough; the latter can be used independently of the rollers to lift mines and turn them out of the vehicle's path. Both types of mine-roller operate at a speed of between 8–11 km/h (5–7 mph).

The Russians anticipate that the flanks of any penetration they effect will be subjected to counter-attack and they therefore intend to defend these by laying minebelts of their own, keeping pace with the level of advance as far as possible. To this end they have developed a number of mechanical minelayer trailer units which are normally towed by a BTR-152 APC. These have a capacity of between 120 and 200 mines which can either be laid on the surface or buried, the space between mines being 4–5.5 m (13–18 ft). Laying a one-kilometre (1,094-yd) surface minebelt takes approximately five minutes, but if the mines are buried only half this distance can be covered during the same period.

The vulnerability of minelayer trailer units led directly to the development of a fully tracked armoured minelayer, the GMZ. This entered service in the mid-1970s and is based on the same chassis as the SA-4 surface-to-air missile system and the 2S3 152 mm self-propelled howitzer. The GMZ has an estimated capacity of 200 mines and a similar performance to the minelaying trailers. The vehicle is manned by a crew of four and is fitted with night vision devices and, probably, an NBC system.

Although frequently referred to in colloquial terms as the Russian Army, the Army of the Union of Soviet Socialist Republics contains elements from approximately one hundred racial groupings. According to the 1979 census the Slav group constitutes 72.2 per cent of the total population, Russians accounting for 52.4, Ukrainians 16.2 and Byelorussians 3.6 per cent. The second largest group, the people of Turkestan, including Uzbeks, Kazakhs, Tajiks, Turkmen and Kirghiz, accounted for 9.9 per cent of the total. After them come the Transcaucasian races (Azeris, Armenians and Georgians) with 5.0 per cent, the Turkik races of the Volga basin (Tatars, Chuvash and Bashkirs) with 3.6 per cent, the Baltic races (Lithuanians, Latvians and Estonians) with 2.0 per cent, the balance being made up by small minorities including Moldavians with 1 per cent, Germans and Jews with 0.7 per cent each and Poles with 0.4 per cent. This balance is changing steadily because the birth rate is falling among the Slav population and rising among the peoples of Central Asia and Trans-caucasia. The demographic trend indicates that by 1995 the proportion of 18-year-old

In tank and motor rifle units only a proportion of the vehicle strength is employed for day-to-day training. Usually this amounts to one platoon per company, the vehicles being grouped in a training company and periodically rotated.

Russian males available for conscription will have fallen to 46 per cent while that drawn from Moslem areas will rise to between 25 and 33 per cent.

The *lingua franca* of the Soviet Army is Russian, which is used exclusively. However, the non-Slav races cling tenaciously to their own language and the proportion of men fluent in Russian as a second language is often less than half and among some races less than one-third. Despite this, recruits are expected to absorb sufficient Russian on their own initiative to be able to perform their duties. A further problem which has arisen in recent years is that of strict Moslem fundamentalism, which provides a constant source of friction between the opposed ideologies of Islam and secular communism.

Although the Soviet Army is proud to present itself as a melting pot of nationalities and cultures united under the banner of a common ideal, there is no disguising the fact that questions of race, language and religion do provoke internal tensions that end in violence and sometimes in killing. The Slavs tend to regard themselves as being a cut above the rest and history has left them with some doubts as to the loyalty and reliability of ethnic minorities. During the Great Patriotic War, for example, it is estimated that the *Wehrmacht* and *Waffen-SS* recruited no fewer than 700,000 non-Slav citizens of the Soviet Union.

The leaders of the Soviet Army avoid these difficulties as far as possible in two important ways. First, units are not recruited on a territorial basis, conscripts being posted to areas remote from their homelands. Secondly, as a matter of policy Slavs constitute four-fifths of the strength of combat formations, the ethnic minorities which form the balance being employed in service and support units. Outside the teeth arms, for example in construction, rear-area engineer and transport units, these proportions are reversed. This naturally places an increasing burden on the Slav element at a time when its proportion of the overall population is in decline but this is not considered to be a major problem in the short term. On the other hand, in a prolonged conflict the reinforcement of hard-hit formations with non-Slavic replacements can be seen as a potential source of trouble.

The backbone of the Soviet Army is its officer corps. The officer receives his commission after spending not less than four years at one of over 150 specialist arm-of-service Higher Military Colleges, which provide a medium-level military education. After several years of regimental service he might be selected for a three-year course at one of 13 Military Academies, which again are specialist in their curricula. Unless he passes this course he is unlikely to be promoted beyond the rank of Major. Following a further period of active duty he might also be selected for the General Staff Academy and if he completes this course satisfactorily the road is open for promotion to the highest ranks. In the periods between formal academic training the officer will attend a variety of courses intended to keep him up to date with current developments, both military and political. The Soviet officer is a privileged member of society but he is also a hard-working and well-educated professional. The senior commanders who fought against the *Wehrmacht* earned the sincere respect of their enemy and there is no reason to suspect that their successors are any the less masters of their craft.

Of particular importance in the Soviet scheme of things are the political officers, who are present at every level down to company and usually occupy the position of the unit's second-in-command. The slightly stupid, bull-necked commissar of Stalin's era, ruling in the Party's name through sheer naked terror, has long since vanished. Instead, today's political officer is qualified in the arm of service to which he is attached and is intelligent, articulate and ambitious. His duties naturally include political lectures, but he is also responsible for his unit's motivation and morale. The Soviet soldier of 1945 hated deeply and needed no encouragement to fight, but now recruits have only inherited memories of the horrors of the Great Patriotic War and must be imbued with the conviction that the West is a real and very dangerous enemy whose aim is the destruction of their country. As it is important that he gains the trust and confidence of the soldiers the political officer also doubles as the unit's welfare officer, obtaining compassionate leave in appropriate circumstances and giving freely of his own spare time to arrange sporting events and other off-duty activities. Because of this more subtle approach the troops respect him and are inclined to believe what he tells them. The ultimate test of the political officer's efficiency rests on how well his unit would fight if the need arose.

The position regarding non-commissioned officers in the Soviet Army is less satisfactory. Although conscripts are offered attractive inducements, including promotion, to extend their period with the colours, few are inclined to do so, and the proportion of non-commissioned soldiers serving as regulars has been put as low as five per cent. Thus, the vast majority of Soviet NCOs are conscripts who have spent the first five months of their service in special training divisions, each of which has the establishment of a motor rifle division. Within the training division each of the component arms trains potential NCOs in the technical skills they will require. Within the tank regiment, for example, the first battalion might run a tank commander's course, the second courses for gunners and radio operators and the third a course for drivers, while other appropriate skills are taught by the motor rifle, artillery, engineer, and other units. On conclusion of their training the potential NCOs sit an examination and depending on their marks they pass out with the rank of Corporal, Junior

Sergeant or Sergeant and are then posted to a combat formation for the remainder of their service. The demand for NCOs is heavy and each training division produces about 20,000 a year.

The proportion of NCOs to private soldiers is high in tank and motor rifle regiments. If a tank is not commanded by an officer it is commanded by a Sergeant, the other members of the crew also being NCOs, with the exception of the loader. In motor rifle regiments equipped with BTR-60 APCs each section has its own Sergeant, while in BMP units each section contains no less than three Sergeants. The function of the Sergeant is to ensure that orders are carried out to the letter, to supervise and to attend to minor administrative matters. Unlike his Western counterpart, who will have spent years achieving his rank and accumulated a vast store of military and man-management experience in the process, the Soviet Sergeant is not invited to venture opinions or advice to his superiors, let alone demonstrate his initiative. Indeed, he is in no

Because the half-yearly intake of conscripts coincides with the release of an equivalent number of trained soldiers, training cycles tend to be repetitive. During his two-year period of service a conscript can expect to complete four training cycles.

position to do so, since he is the same age as and has no more practical experience than his young soldiers and in any event will only be with his unit for a maximum of 18 months.

Such a lack of continuity and accumulated experience in an era when weapon technology is subject to constant change is a matter of serious concern to the leadership of the Soviet Army, yet it has little alternative other than to persevere with the policy of expediency in the creation of NCOs. An attempt to bridge this gap began in 1971 with the revival of the old rank of Ensign, which is the approximate equivalent of Warrant Officer in Western armies. The qualified regular Sergeant who wishes to become an ensign must complete a one-year course but will then enjoy many of the officers' privileges and carry out some of their duties, including the supervision of NCOs, and remain with his unit for most of his engagement. In suitable cases, individual Ensigns may go on to achieve commissioned rank.

Unlike the majority of the rank and file who fought in the Great Patriotic War, today's conscripts have enjoyed the benefit of a full secondary education and are both literate and numerate. Since 1945 living standards have also improved dramatically but any tendency towards softness induced by comparatively comfortable living is swiftly eliminated by the hard conditions in which the conscript is expected to serve and which ensure that the Soviet soldier has lost none of his legendary toughness and stoicism. Soviet citizens may not all enjoy their period of conscription but they accept it as a normal part of their lives.

Unless he has received exemption or deferment, the conscript enters the Army shortly after his 18th birthday. He serves for two years and then remains on the reserve until he is 50, attending refresher courses from time to time. Inductions take place twice yearly, in May and November. The conscript's first month is spent learning the basics of military life and at the end of this period he will publicly take his Soldier's Oath at a formal parade attended, if possible, by his family. If he has been selected as a potential NCO he will then be posted to a training division but if not he will proceed direct to his combat division where he will be trained *in situ*. In either event he will find that discipline is extremely strict and that the NCOs are not averse to using their fists to enforce it. In combat divisions bullying of new arrivals by earlier previous intakes is said to be

endemic. This sort of thing, coupled with the kind of mindless 'bull' long since abandoned by professional Western armies, the absence of home leave and the fact that he is virtually confined to barracks when he is not in the field, provides few incentives for the conscript to make the Army his career.

One especially vexatious problem which troubles the Soviet Army is that because of the dimensions of its armoured vehicles, and particularly its tanks and APCs, they are crewed most efficiently by men of below average height; in the case of the T-72, for example, an upper limit of 5 ft 4 in has been mentioned, and that for other AFVs currently in service cannot be very different. This difficulty is aggravated by the fact that in the western republics of the USSR, the Slav heartland, the standard of living has improved steadily since 1945 with the result that, in common with Europe generally, the average height of the population has tended to rise. This is less apparent in the races of Central Asia and Transcaucasia yet historical distrust, the language barrier and lack of a technical background renders then ineligible to fill the gap. Against this, the simple, robust, soldier-proof design of Soviet AFVs renders them very suitable for training large numbers of men from different backgrounds in crew trades in the minimum possible time.

Within combat divisions training takes place in repetitive six-monthly cycles. These begin with individual and crew training, followed by platoon and company training, then battalion and regimental training, and finally with large-scale exercises which are held twice yearly and involve the entire division in manoeuvres which might extend as high as army or front level. At the end of the cycle the time-expired conscripts, accounting for approximately one-quarter of the division's strength, are returned to civilian life. This is an extremely frustrating process for senior officers who have worked hard to bring their formations and units to the peak of efficiency only to lose so high a proportion of their most experienced men the

Overleaf:
Major exercises make a welcome break in routine, even in conditions as hard as this. T-72s advance at speed during Exercise 'Berezina'. The side plates which normally cover the upper suspension have been removed, probably to prevent compaction of ice and snow *(Novosti).*

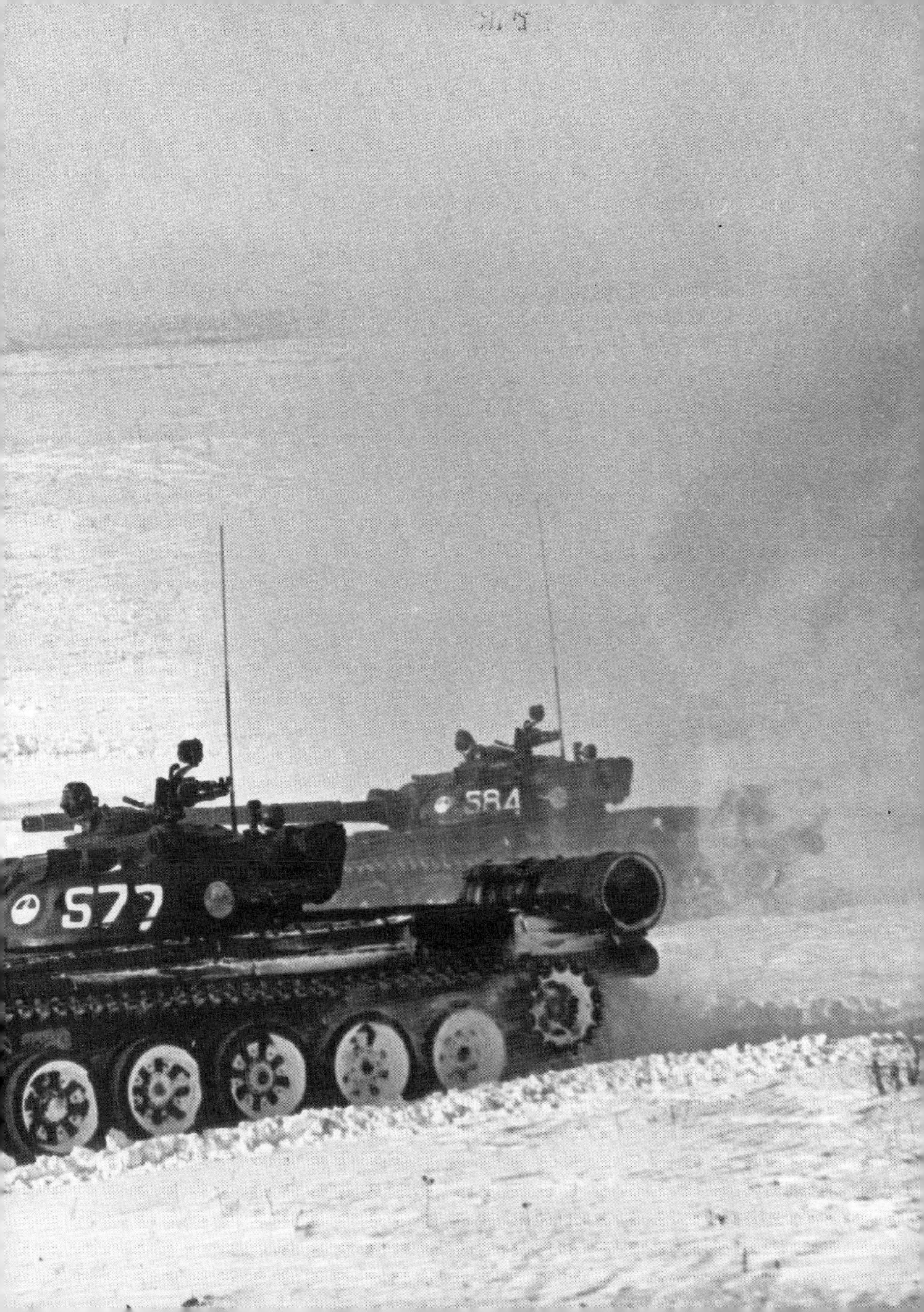
S77
S84

minute they have achieved their object, their places being taken by an equivalent number of raw recruits. It is equally frustrating for the conscripts who have to perform the same training programme over the same ground every six months.

The expenditure involved in training the Soviet Army is enormous and every effort is made to contain it. Tank gunners, for instance, are lucky if they fire half-a-dozen live rounds in a year. Training simulators are widely used for all crew trades and, in appropriate circumstances, older vehicles and weapons are employed on tactical demonstrations to reduce wear and tear on newer equipment. Unless units are fully committed to major exercises only part of their vehicle strength is actually used for day-to-day training while the rest remains in its hangars. In tank and motor rifle

units this proportion amounts to one platoon per company, the vehicles usually being grouped together as a training company and rotated periodically with those in reserve. Human nature being what it is, the danger exists that those vehicles used for training will be hammered until they develop serious faults and break down, while those in reserve begin to suffer from extra-tightened nuts and other aspects of over-maintenance which will only become apparent when they are taken out.

The Soviet Army, like any other, is well aware of the importance of tradition and *esprit de corps*, both of which it seeks to foster. Apart from the weapons carried, a unit on full-dress parade with its colours and band bears a startling resemblance to one of the Tsar's regiments, and is perhaps even a little smarter. Conscripts are told the story of their unit's

T-55s and BTR-60PBs demonstrate the classic Soviet dismounted attack during Exercise 'Carpaty', July 1977. Such attacks are usually mounted approximately 1,000 m (1,094 yd) short of the objective with tanks and APCs providing close supporting fire *(Novosti)*.

battle honours and the meaning of such honorific titles as Guards, which were conferred on formations for outstanding service during the Great Patriotic War, the object being to instill in the young soldiers that they are the heirs to these great fighting traditions. In the overall context these measures are of undoubted value but they do not generate anything like the fierce regimental pride so highly developed by the British Army nor the divisional spirit prized by the American and German armies, partly because Soviet conscripts are not with their units long enough for any sense of family to develop, and partly because the units themselves are deliberately not recruited on a local basis, a policy which deprives them of an ex-service infrastructure and the concentrated moral support of a civil population which can identify with them. Nonetheless, the élite status of tank formations is publicly acknowledged by an annual holiday, Soviet Tankmen's Day, which takes place during the second week of September.

Below the political-military directorate and the *Stavka* or General Staff, the highest level of command in the Soviet Army is that of Commander-in-Chief of a Strategic Direction, which is the equivalent of a theatre of war. Each Strategic Direction controls several fronts, which equate with army groups in Western terms. Each front contains several armies which consist of a variable number of tank and motor rifle divisions and are the approximate equivalent of Western corps, although the divisions themselves are somewhat smaller than their NATO counterparts.

The Tables in the Annex show a representative outline of the order of battle for both types of Soviet division.

In addition to these formations army commanders have an independent tank regiment of three battalions at their disposal and each front has an independent tank brigade consisting of four or five tank battalions and a motor rifle battalion.

It can be seen from the tables in the Annex that despite the varying proportions of tanks to motor rifle troops the two types of division are remarkably similar and either can be augmented with further tank, motor rifle or artillery units to the point where the difference between the two becomes academic. At the higher levels the difference between tank and all-arms armies is equally slight. In fact, now that tank, motor rifle and engineer elements are so closely integrated within formations, units and subunits, Soviet officers are actively encouraged to pursue their careers on an all-arms basis rather than remaining with their original arm throughout their service. This trend in official policy became apparent in 1980 when the title of Chief of Tank Troops was broadened to that of Chief of the Main Armour Directorate, and in 1984 the traditional separate ranks for Tank Troops, Engineers, Signals and Technical Troops were abolished.

During Hitler's invasion of the USSR in 1941 the Soviet armoured corps came very close to being annihilated and in the long and bloody period of reconstruction that followed a searching analysis was made of the reasons for successive large-scale defeats and the precise means by which the *Wehrmacht* had obtained its victories. Inevitably, this led to a restatement of the views promulgated by Triandafillov and further developed by the late and officially discredited Marshal Tukhachevsky, reinforced by the example of Zhukov's decisive victory over the Japanese in 1939. The application of these within the limitations imposed by the centralised Soviet command structure and poor communications network nonethe-less did much to restore a self-confidence which grew as the war progressed. After the great tank battle of Kursk in July 1943 the strategic initiative passed irrevocably to the Soviet Army. At the lower command levels the Soviets also regularly attained their operative objectives despite being worsted by German expertise in numerous tactical encounters. In part this was assisted by Hitler's rigid control of his commanders and the *Luftwaffe*'s declining influence over the battlefields of Eastern Europe, but this does not detract from the scale of the Soviet achievement.

It was during this period that the foundations of the present-day Soviet theory of armoured warfare were laid and many of the

The 1968 invasion of Czechoslovakia was as notable for the speed with which it was executed as for the overwhelming strength with which it was made. Tank crews had been told they were liberators and were genuinely surprised by the hostile reception they received *(AP).*

principles established then remain unaltered. Of these, the most important consideration in the planning of offensive operations is the need to achieve surprise in the broadest possible sense. This includes surprise at the strategic, operative and tactical levels, surprise as to the date, time and place of an attack, and surprise as to the direction a successful attack will be exploited.

The Kremlin is well aware of von Moltke's dictum that an army caught wrongly deployed at the outbreak of a war invariably suffers defeat and for this reason is unlikely to launch an attack until a potential enemy's guard has been lowered. Thus, surprise was achieved during the Warsaw Pact's invasion of Czechoslovakia in 1968 and again during the invasion of Afghanistan in 1979. Against NATO the Warsaw Pact has less chance of achieving surprise on the all-important Central Front because of continuous satellite and electronic surveillance which would give early warning of mobilisation and troop movements. On the other hand, NATO requires 48 hours to reach full combat effectiveness and surprise *is* possible if the so-called 'standing start' option is exercised. This would involve the divisions of the Group of Soviet Forces Germany (GSFG) and reliable allied formations taking the field as though on routine exercise and then breaking through the border after nightfall. The effect would be to give the invaders a full night's running relatively free from air attack, at the end of which they would be well on their way west while the NATO ground troops were still assembling. As to the timing of such an attack, several possibilities present themselves, including a period of détente when relations between East and West are at their most relaxed, the period before an American presidential election, a German bank holiday when crowded autobahns make military movement extremely difficult and, best of all, the Christmas period, when large numbers of men are on leave or involved in celebrations; the potentially catastrophic effects of the Arab attack on Israel during Yom Kippur 1973 need no further emphasis.

The second commandment of the Soviet theory of armoured warfare is that once surprise has been achieved it must be ruthlessly exploited, so turning the enemy's temporary disarray into permanent disruption. This is attained not only by the weight of the blow but also by the speed with which it is delivered and by the distance it travels. In 1943, when the Soviet Army went over to the attack in the aftermath of Kursk, fronts conducted offensives to a depth of 25–32 km (15–20 miles) with a view to encircling up to a dozen German divisions. By 1944, confidence had been restored to such an extent that fronts executed operations to a depth of 160–320 km (100–200 miles), entrapping up to 18 German divisions in the process, while the objectives set for each of their component armies might involve an advance of approximately half this distance and the encirclement of up to six enemy divisions. A major offensive could involve a front advancing between 400–480 km (250–300 miles) in two to three weeks, while an army might cover approximately 160 km (100 miles) in one or two weeks, giving *minimum* average daily running figures of respectively 19 km (12 miles) and 11 km (7 miles). Today, should the Warsaw Pact spearheads break through NATO's main defensive zone, they are expected to advance at a daily rate of between 32 and 48 km (20 and 30 miles).

One of the problems facing the planners of any offensive is that because of battle casualties, mechanical breakdowns and logistic considerations, its power tends to diminish in proportion to the distance it has covered. During the last years of the Great Patriotic War the Soviets sought to minimise the effects of this process by attacking in successive echelons, thereby maintaining the momentum of the advance by passing fresh formations through those which had completed their tasks and been written down while so doing. This process remains a crucial part of the Soviet military philosophy with the echelon system being practised at every level down to regiment. Thus, a front commander might designate two or more armies as his second echelon, an army commander two or more divisions, a divisional commander one or more regimental groups and a regimental commander one or more battalion groups.

Another method by which the Soviets maintain the momentum of the offensive is by means of simultaneous action throughout the entire depth of the enemy's position. This can involve parachute drops by elements of the Airborne Forces, large-scale air-mobile operations by the helicopter-lifted Airborne Assault Brigades, and insertion of commando detachments ahead of the advancing armour, the object being the elimination of headquar-

ters, nuclear weapon sites and airfields, the capture of bridges and other important topographical features and the creation of a climate of chaos before the main issue is joined. One example of this took place during the Warsaw Pact's invasion of Czechoslovakia in 1968, when no less than seven airborne landings, involving the capture of Prague airport and other communications centres, coincided with the crossing of the frontier. Another occurred during the invasion of Afghanistan in 1979 when the Bagram air base near Kabul was seized by the 105th Guards Airborne Division, some elements of which then occupied the capital while others drove north to secure the strategically important Salang Tunnel, through which the 201st and 360th Motor Rifle Divisions must pass on their way south.

The keynote of offensive operations is continuous movement. During the period when the Soviets were developing the full potential of their offensive techniques against the *Wehrmacht* their encirclements initially consisted of two cordons, one to contain the trapped German divisions and the other to ward off relief attempts. Later, the outer cordon was found to be unnecessary and was abandoned as a waste

of resources. Today, the formations leading a Soviet offensive will do little more than screen enemy forces which they have bypassed, leaving them to be dealt with by succeeding echelons. Whenever possible, movement will be maintained through the hours of darkness, which provide some protection against air attack. As we have seen, Soviet AFVs are well equipped for night fighting and a high proportion of training takes place at night.

Offensives are conducted along axes which have been predetermined during the planning stage, taking into account terrain, the avoidance of built-up areas and the probable deployment of the enemy. On a primary axis an army might have a frontage of 32 km (20 miles) but on a secondary axis this might extend as far as 80 km (50 miles). The army's first echelon normally consists of two divisions each of which has been allocated two parallel routes forward, using roads whenever possible. The advance is made in column of route and units will only deploy from this if they are about to attack. Much emphasis is placed on the need for rapid deployment as a means of maintaining momentum and orders of march have been standardised with this in mind.

In Afghanistan tanks proved to be of less use than armoured personnel carriers in the kind of war being waged and the majority were withdrawn to the Soviet Union. This T-62 regiment is seen on the road between Kabul and the frontier *(Novosti)*.

The leading element of the advance is the divisional reconnaissance battalion, which may operate up to 48 km (30 miles) ahead of its main body and cover a frontage of between 16 and 24 km (10 and 15 miles). The remainder of the division generally moves in three regimental groups, each led by a close reconnaissance patrol and consisting of an advance guard, the first battalion group, regimental headquarters, etc., the second battalion group, the third battalion group, the regimental logistics group, flank and rear guards. Battalion groups contain elements of all arms and are MBT- or APC-heavy depending on whether the division is tank or motor rifle. The leading battalion group has the additional task of providing troops for the advance guard and is reinforced with NBC reconnaissance troops and engineer units which deal with obstacles or demolitions encountered along the line of march. Those artillery, engineer and air defence units which have not been allocated to the battalion groups travel in the same part of the column as regimental headquarters. The close reconnaissance patrol normally operates 5 km (3 miles) ahead of the leading units of the advance guard, which operates a similar distance ahead of the first battalion group. This is separated from the regimental headquarters group by a gap of 10–16 km (6–10 miles), with further gaps of approximately 3 km (2 miles) between the remaining groups of the regimental column. An army advancing in two echelons has an approximate depth, front to rear, of 96 km (60 miles), with army reconnaissance units covering the outer flanks and the spaces between divisions.

For specific missions ahead of their main body the Soviets employ two types of force which are formed quickly from local resources. The first of these is the Forward Detachment, which consists of a reinforced tank or motor rifle battalion group complete with its own reconnaissance, artillery, engineer and NBC elements. This operates at divisional level and the troops involved are usually drawn from the second echelon so as to preserve the integrity of the division's leading regiments. The task of

Although the ASU-85 is not amphibious it can ford to a depth of 1.1 m (3 ft 8 in) without preparation (*Novosti*).

Soviet infantrymen
double past their IFV
for a dismounted attack.

the Forward Detachment is to penetrate the enemy hinterland to a depth of 30–48 km (20–30 miles), seize important bridges or other features and hold them until relieved.

The second is the Operational Manoeuvre Group (OMG), which has a number of precedents in Russian military history. The purpose of the OMG is to destabilise the enemy's command and control apparatus at the critical moment by creating a serious threat in his rear areas at the very time his attention is fully occupied by the threat developing along his front. This can be achieved by a direct attack on command and logistic areas, or by engaging reserves as they move forward to join in the battle, or by establishing a blocking position behind formations that are already fully committed. Ideally, OMGs should break through lightly defended sectors of the front during the early hours of an offensive and co-operate with simultaneous operations involving the airmobile Airborne Assault Brigades. Like Forward Detachments, OMGs are organised on an all-arms basis, with the troops involved only being detailed for the role at the last possible moment. In theory, the size of the OMG is infinite; a front might employ two or more divisions as its OMG, an army might employ one, and a division might employ the major part of its second echelon.

If the Warsaw Pact does succeed in taking NATO by surprise, the first engagements will inevitably occur while the latter's forces are attempting to move into their battle positions, and for this reason the Soviets stress the importance of what they call the Meeting Engagement or, in Western parlance, the Encounter Battle. This will develop when the reconnaissance troops first meet serious opposition. The regimental advance guard will close up and attempt to fight its way through. If it fails it will continue to fight a holding action with the defenders. Under cover of this the artillery deploys to fire positions and the reconnaissance units guide the main body of the regiment to a position from which the enemy's flank can be assaulted, normally by two battalion groups in succession. Battalion groups commence their deployment about 5 km (3 miles) from the enemy position by splitting into parallel company columns with the tanks leading. When they are approximately 2.5 km (1.5 miles) short of the objective the company columns sub-divide into parallel platoon columns which deploy into line abreast 914 m (1,000 yd) from the objective. The assault is delivered with the tanks leading and the APCs following close behind. If resistance is slight the infantry remain aboard their APCs and fire on the move, but if it is heavy the situation may demand a dismounted assault with the tanks and APCs giving close support. Throughout these moves the objective will have come under preparatory fire from artillery, rocket launchers, mortars, helicopters and ground-attack aircraft, while the assault itself is delivered behind a rolling barrage. If the attack is a success a breakthrough will be achieved and the momentum of the advance restored, the enemy survivors being left to be dealt with by the next echelon or pursued until they are destroyed. A regimental attack such as this takes between one and two hours to mount, but if the enemy is present in such strength as to warrant a full divisional attack this can take up to four hours to prepare.

Naturally, the Soviet Army's doctrine of the offensive demands overwhelming local superiority along its chosen thrust lines. During their 1944 operations against the *Wehrmacht* the Soviets were able to establish local superiorities in the ratio of 6–8:1 in tanks and artillery, 3–5:1 in combat aircraft and 3–5:1 in manpower. In Germany today the Warsaw Pact deploys 17,500 tanks against NATO's 7,000, a ratio of 2.5:1; 7,500 artillery weapons against 2,700 (2.8:1); 2,700 fixed-wing combat aircraft against 1,150 (2.3:1); and 950,000 men against 780,000 (1.5:1). However, the Warsaw Pact is only able to deploy 200 armed helicopters against NATO's 400 and 1,200 ATGW launchers against 4,000, giving respectively unfavourable odds of 1:2 and 1:3.1.

In their book *Not Over by Christmas – NATO's Central Front in World War III*, Elmar Dinter and Paddy Griffith estimate that if both armies were to be reinforced over a period of 30 days the number of weapon systems and men would rise dramatically but there would be no radical alteration in the ratios quoted above. Thus, 30,000 Warsaw Pact tanks would be deployed against NATO's 10,000, a ratio of 3:1; 17,000 artillery weapons against 4,000 (4.2:1); 7,000 fixed-wing combat aircraft against 3,500 (2:1); 600 armed helicopters against 800 (1:1.3); 1,500 ATGW launchers against 4,600 (1:3.1); and 2,200,000 men against 1,900,000 (1.2:1).

As such a degree of mobilisation would obviously forfeit surprise without markedly increasing the odds in their favour, many Soviet commanders may feel that it is counterproductive and prefer to retain the element of surprise while relying on their present superiority, which is in any event close enough to the ratio of 3:1 which is traditionally estimated to be required for a successful offensive. On the other hand, others may point to NATO's superiority in anti-tank weapons and general proficiency in tank gunnery and, mindful of the fearful losses inflicted by the *Wehrmacht* in 1944 when the odds were even more heavily weighted in the Soviet Army's favour, regard the present ratio as inadequate. Against this, some analysts contend that a better reflection of the comparative relationship between opposed armies is obtained by calculating the square of their strengths.

This returns us to the point at which it can be seen that the Warsaw Pact can achieve the local superiorities it requires, and with comparative ease. Taking the point, together with the structure of divisions, the limited combat employment expected of each and the echeloned nature of offensives, the whole underlines the Soviet Army's philosophy that it is prepared to sustain tactical defeats and incur heavy casualties while so doing, especially among the leading echelons, as long as it wins its battles at the operative level and thereby attains its strategic objective. In other words, it simply does not matter if a particular division is torn to pieces, provided the army of which it forms part can complete its share of the planned offensive.

The Soviet concept of static defence follows that of the majority of armies, relying on depth, mutual support by all arms and the channelling of enemy attacks on to artillery and anti-tank killing grounds by means of terrain features and minefields. However, as the thrust of Soviet military thought is offensive and its ultimate object is a quick victory in the *Blitzkrieg* tradition, the holding of ground is regarded as being a temporary expedient undertaken because of local difficulties. Having been counter-attacked, the Soviets prefer to respond with a counter-attack of their own, so re-creating the conditions of the Meeting Engagement and regaining the initiative.

Nonetheless, however well the Soviet Army might be equipped and structured for high-speed, deep-penetration operations these are by their very nature extremely demanding of those required to carry them out, especially so in the intangible areas of personal initiative, flexibility, command, control and communications, and it is these very areas that the Soviets could well find themselves at a disadvantage in any confrontation with NATO.

A Guards airborne regiment rolls past the Kremlin in its BMD IFVs, 7 November 1983. The vehicles appear to be fitted with Spandrel ATGW launchers. The Airborne Forces insignia is painted on the hull sides and turret hatches *(Novosti)*.

Initiative is a particularly thorny problem for the Soviets, for although they recognise its value the concept is at variance with Marxist–Leninist dogma, which demands the centralised planning of every stage of military operations, the execution of which might be prejudiced by the introduction of some local variation by a subordinate commander. This was probably necessary during the last two years of the Great Patriotic War, when the famine of radio sets meant that every offensive had to be carefully rehearsed and was extremely difficult to control once it had been set in motion. To an extent the Soviets were able to overcome some of the problems encountered by attaching liaison officers to the headquarters of the various subordinate command levels. These officers knew the workings of the

front commander's mind and how he intended to attain his designated objectives, and within these parameters were able to sanction or reject alternative solutions proposed by lower formation commanders. Although this conferred some degree of flexibility, it fell well below that found in the armies of Germany or the Western Allies and all too often dogmatism resulted in heavy casualties arising from repeated and frequently pointless attacks made over the same ground.

Since then the communications apparatus of the Soviet Army has improved beyond recognition. In Category I divisions at least each tank and APC has its own radio set, although below the level of company commander these are simply receivers. Again, while the detailed plans for an offensive are still made centrally,

Polish T-72s on exercise. The T-72 is equipped with a small dozer blade which is folded flat against the bow plate when not in use. All Warsaw Pact tanks are now fitted with radio sets *(Wojskowa Agencja Fotograficzna)*.

the nature of this has meant that subordinate commanders enjoy greater latitude than of yore. For example, the speed demanded in the all-important Meeting Engagement requires that the regimental commander should be master in his own house, but below regimental level the use of personal initiative is not encouraged and all that is demanded of junior officers in action is that they should stick to the regimental plan. In Western armies, if the need arises subalterns are expected to take over their companies and company commanders their battalions, using their instinct and judgement as the situation warrants. Against this, the

Soviets argue that the company or battalion battle has comparatively less importance for them in the overall context, especially if the assault is in motion. This, however, ignores the broader aspects of the matter, for the regimental, battalion and company commanders' vehicles can quickly be identified and are the primary target of NATO tank gunners and ATGW teams, ensuring that both the chain of command and the communications net are broken. Such circumstances do not merit a robotic obedience to orders but require outstanding junior leadership, which may or may not be forthcoming.

Although the Soviet Army has not fought a major war since 1945 it has amassed considerable experience of armoured warfare during the past 40 years in which both the validity of its theories and the performance of its AFVs have been thoroughly tested, with varying results. This has been achieved by direct involvement in a comparatively few cases, more frequently by the use of advisers attached to surrogate forces or others fighting for communist objectives, and more frequently

still by means of instructors serving with the armies of belligerent client states.

The first engagements involving Soviet-built armour since the end of World War 2 took place during the opening months of the Korean War, 1950–53. Spearheaded by 150 T-34/85s, the North Korean People's Army invaded South Korea on 25 June 1950 and for a while swept all before it. The South Koreans had virtually no armour of their own, nor did they possess effective anti-tank weapons, so

An M-26 Pershing edges past an abandoned T-34/85 on a Korean road. A demolition charge has been exploded inside the T-34's main armament, causing it to 'banana' (USAMHI).

Hungarian civilians crowd round T-34s in Budapest during the October 1956 uprising. Units which had such contacts with the civil population were considered unreliable by the Kremlin and were withdrawn prior to the main Soviet invasion.

imeter until the United Nations landing at Inchon, on the west coast of Korea, on 15 September 1950. The following day the Eighth Army, as the allied forces in Pusan were now known, went over to the offensive, trapping the communists between the hammer and the anvil. Caught completely off balance, the routed North Koreans fled back across the border, abandoning such of their armour as had not already been destroyed, their AFV losses accounting to 239 T-34s and 74 SU-76s.

The conflict in Korea had almost three years to run but after 1950 communist armour played only a minor supportive role in what became a positional war of attrition. This, however, cannot disguise the fact that the original North Korean offensive failed by the narrowest of margins, and that had it succeeded the world would have been presented with a *fait accompli*.

On the other side of the world, serious anti-communist riots broke out in East Berlin on 16/17 June 1953. The Soviets wasted no time in sending tank units to clear the streets, which they did quickly and ruthlessly, killing and wounding several hundred civilians in the process. Three years later, on 28/29 June 1956, similar disturbances took place in Poznan, Poland, and were dealt with in the same brutal fashion, 50 civilians being killed and hundreds were injured.

A third, and far more serious, explosion of discontent in Eastern Europe took the form of a full-scale rebellion in Hungary, commencing on 23 October 1956. The Soviets reacted as they had in Berlin and Poznan by sending their tanks into Budapest but dangerously under-estimated both the strength and motivation of their opponents, simultaneously forgetting a major lesson of World War 2, namely that tanks, with their numerous blind spots, are at a serious disadvantage during fighting in built-up areas unless they are closely supported by infantry. Furthermore, the insurgents proved adept at restricting the tanks' movements within the city by lowering live tramway cables into their path, using tramcars as barricades, laying dummy minefields across roadways using up-turned soup plates and pan lids, and pouring liquid soap over the cobbles so that the steel tracks spun uselessly. Then, while tank commanders were kept pinned inside their cupolas by sniper fire, Molotov cocktails would be used to set their vehicles ablaze. In other instances groups of civilians surrounded

that the communist tanks were able to smash their way through one position after another without troubling to deploy. Newly arrived American units managed to slow down the North Korean advance but could not halt it as the only tanks available at first were light M24 Chaffees which were no match for the T-34s, while the infantry were equipped with the obsolete 2.36 in bazooka which proved to be useless against the Soviet armour even at point-blank range. However, as more divisions began to pour into the country a defensive perimeter was established around the port of Pusan, and fierce fighting raged around this.

Having been reinforced with a further 80 T-34s and a number of SU-76 self-propelled howitzers, the North Koreans attempted to deliver the *coup de grâce*. The early encounters had left the Americans with the uneasy feeling that the T-34 was impervious to their weapons, but now the balance was slowly but surely restored by the intervention of ground-attack aircraft, the arrival of better tanks in the form of M4A3 76 mm Shermans and M26 90 mm Pershings, and the issue of the new 3.5 in anti-tank rocket launcher. During August a series of engagements at Obong-ni Ridge near Yongson and in a valley near Taegu known as 'The Bowling Alley' resulted in the destruction of a considerable number of T-34s by ground-attack aircraft and the fire of M26 tanks and 3.5 in rocket launchers, re-establishing American confidence and shattering the legend of the Russian tank's invulnerability.

Nonetheless, the North Koreans continued to maintain their pressure against the per-

An IS-3 blown apart by
an internal explosion
during the street
fighting in Budapest
(AP).

T-54 tanks and BTR-152
APCs parked in a
Budapest street. After
their early losses the
Soviets provided tanks
with a close infantry
escort during the street
battles.

Soviet vehicles and talked their crews round to a sympathetic viewpoint.

By the 28th there were signs that the Soviets were prepared to withdraw from Hungary but these were merely a ploy, for the Kremlin was determined to stamp out the revolt, assembling twelve divisions and 3,000 tanks for the purpose. On 1 November this force invaded and fought a conventional war against the insurgents which reduced much of Budapest to ruins. Using the same tank/infantry tactics supported by artillery with which they had stormed Berlin in 1945, the Soviets ground their way from block to block against courageous but hopeless resistance. By 14 November the rebellion had been crushed. About 2,000 Hungarians died in Budapest and a further 1,000 in other part of the country, with possibly three times these numbers being wounded. Soviet casualties are unknown but probably total several hundred killed and perhaps 40 tanks destroyed.

Simultaneously, war had broken out in the Middle East between Egypt on the one hand and Israel, France and the United Kingdom on the other, the causes being respectively the closure of the Straits of Tiran to Israeli shipping and President Nasser's nationalisation of the Suez Canal Company. On the eve of hostilities Egypt possessed 430 tanks and 300 tank destroyers, including 150 T-34/85s, 50 IS-3s and 100 SU-100 tank destroyers which had been purchased through the agency of Czechoslovakia the previous year, together with 200 BTR-152 APCs. Much of this was retained in Egypt to counter the Anglo-French threat, but in Sinai tank and tank destroyer

battalions were attached to the 8th Palestinian Infantry Division in the Gaza Strip and the 3rd Infantry Division in the area El Arish–Abu Agheila, while the 1st Armoured Brigade, consisting of two T-34/85 battalions, an APC battalion and an SU-100 company, was positioned in immediate reserve at Bir Gifgafa.

The basis of the allied strategy was that Israel should invade Sinai with the ultimate object of re-opening the Straits of Tiran, while British and French troops landed at Port Said, ostensibly to put an end to the fighting and protect the Suez Canal. The Israeli operational plan consisted of four phases, the first of which involved the seizure of the eastern end of the Mitla Pass by a parachute brigade, so denying Egyptian reinforcements access to central Sinai; phase two required the capture of the strongly fortified Egyptian position at Abu Agheila, followed by an advance westwards across central Sinai; phase three required the destruction of the Egyptian forces in the Gaza Strip followed by an advance along the coast road; and phase four would consist of an advance to Sharm el Sheikh, on the southern tip of the Sinai Peninsula, intended to re-open the Straits.

The offensive opened with the dropping of a single parachute battalion at the Mitla Pass during the evening of 29 October. This quickly seized its objective while the rest of its parent brigade advanced overland to join it, capturing El Kuntilla, El Thamad and Nakhl along the way. At Nakhl several BTR-152s were captured intact and promptly substituted for the labouring civilian buses in which some units were travelling. The brigade joined its isolated battalion at the pass shortly before midnight on 30 October and consolidated its hold on the position.

At Abu Agheila the Egyptians resisted fiercely and it was not until the night of 1 November that the last of their defences were cleared. During the fighting a battalion of T-34/85s had attempted to break through to the embattled garrison from the direction of El Arish but had been halted in a long-range gunnery duel. Fighting in the Gaza Strip was also severe and continued until 2 November, but by then the Israeli armour, consisting of approximately 100 up-gunned Shermans and 100 AMX-13s, was already advancing rapidly across northern and central Sinai.

No major tank battle took place because at this point the Egyptian High Command lost its nerve following the start of the Anglo-French bombing attacks against its air bases. It had committed its 1st Mechanised Division to the Sinai front on the outbreak of hostilities but no sooner had the division reached El Arish after being strafed by Israeli aircraft *en route* than it received orders to retire behind the Canal. Similar orders were received by the 1st Armoured Brigade, which had actually left its base at Bir Gifgafa to join in the fighting. During their hasty withdrawal the Egyptians were constantly harassed by air attacks. As agreed with their allies, the Israelis halted their advance 16 km (10 miles) east of the Canal and by 4 November had secured their final objective, Sharm el Sheikh. The equipment captured in Sinai included 100 tanks and tank destroyers, and a large number of APCs.

The Anglo-French invasion of Egypt began on 5 November with parachute drops on Port Said and Port Fuad, followed the next day by seaborne landings. In some areas resistance was protracted but Egyptian armour took little part in the fighting. On the British sector a dug-in SU-100 tank destroyer was silenced by naval gunfire, while four tanks which were unwisely engaging the French from the Anglo-American Oil Company's tank farm met a spectacular end when the huge fuel containers ruptured and exploded under air attack. Throughout 7 November both contingents pushed south down the Canal against negligible opposition, covering half its length, but were reluctantly forced to halt at midnight in compliance with a United Nations' ceasefire demand.

After the Suez Affair, British and French influence throughout the Middle East declined sharply. Nasser, who had sustained a serious military defeat, emerged as the political victor and the champion of the Arab world while the Soviet Union willingly supplied arms and instructors to every Arab nation which asked for them. However, by no means all Arabs wished to follow a Marxist path and in 1962 a protracted civil war broke out in Yemen between monarchist and communist factions, the former supported by Saudi Arabia and the latter by Egypt. Nasser contributed an expeditionary force which eventually numbered 35,000 men and included a substantial armoured element, but this did not acquit itself well and incurred heavy casualties before being withdrawn.

Meanwhile, in 1959 Fidel Castro had seized power in the Caribbean island of Cuba. A breach with the United States soon followed and he turned to the Soviet Union for assistance, receiving large supplies of arms and military equipment, including 25 T-34/85s. On 15 April 1961 a 1,500-strong group of Cuban exiles, armed and trained by the United States, landed in the Bahia de Cochinas (Bay of Pigs), hoping to provoke an insurrection. This proved to be wildly optimistic and Castro was quickly able to assemble a force of 2,000 men, supported by 20 tanks and artillery, and led them against the invaders. The exiles fought well, ambushing the approaching columns and all but annihilating one of them, but exhausted their ammunition. By the 20th it was clear that the coup had failed and the survivors were rounded up as they attempted to reach the mountains in small groups.

The affair inevitably pushed Cuba even further into the Soviet camp and this in turn provoked the Missile Crisis of 1962. However, the subsequent cost to the Soviet Union of maintaining the Cuban economy has been heavy and the Kremlin has required that Cuba should earn her keep by providing surrogate forces whenever the Soviet interest demands it.

By 1967 the situation in the Middle East had deteriorated so seriously that Israel, faced with the prospect of simultaneous attack by Egypt, Jordan and Syria, decided to mount a preemptive strike. In Sinai the Egyptian Army, thanks to the ample supply of Soviet arms, was far stronger than it had been in 1956, but was similarly deployed with strong emphasis on defence in depth in the manner of Kursk.

Altogether, seven divisions were positioned close to the frontier: the 20th Palestinian Infantry Division, with 50 Shermans, in the Gaza Strip; the 7th Infantry Division, with 100 T-34/85s and IS-3s, covering the road junction at Rafah, the Jiradi defile and El Arish; the 2nd Infantry Division, with 100 T-35/85s and T-54s, at Abu Agheila, and the 3rd Infantry Division, with a similar tank component, immediately to its west at Jebel Libni; the 6th Mechanised Division, again with 100 T-34/85s and T-54s, at El Kuntilla and Nakhl; a group known as Task Force Shazli with 150 T-55s, positioned between El Quseima and El Kuntilla; and 4th Armoured Division, the principal counter-attack force, with 200 T-55s, based at Bar Gifgafa. Including reserves, the total tank strength available amounted to 950 vehicles (50 Shermans, 300

T-34/85s, 400 T-54/55s, 100 IS-3s and 100 SU-100s) but the basic flaw in the Egyptian disposition was that the majority were subordinate to local infantry commanders, leaving only 350 serving in armoured formations. In contrast, the Israeli Army's Southern Command possessed a total of 680 tanks (Centurions, M48 Pattons, up-gunned Shermans and AMX-13s), all of which were serving in armoured formations, and the majority in three armoured divisions.

The Six Day War began on 5 June 1967 with a series of strikes by the Israeli Air Force which effectively destroyed the Arabs' air power. These coincided with an advance across the Egyptian frontier by three armoured divisions, leaving the Gaza Strip to be cleared later. El Arish was captured ahead of schedule and Abu Agheila fell the same night. The Egyptian 4th Armoured Division attempted to intervene but was ambushed and severely mauled during its night approach march, then bundled westward until its remnants were destroyed near Bir Gifgafa. Having broken through the Egyptian defences, the Israeli armour advanced steadily across Sinai through the wreck of the beaten army, seizing the Mitla, Giddi and Tassa passes to prevent its retreat, and by 8 June had established itself along the Canal. Constantly harried by air attacks, the Egyptian survivors began flooding west only to find themselves trapped. Desperate attempts to fight their way through the Mitla Pass by fugitives from several divisions all ended in failure and ultimate surrender. At the strategic level the Egyptian command had simply been unable to respond to the speed with which events developed, while in tactical encounters its tanks were repeatedly out-manoeuvred in the sort of fast-moving battle for which their crews had not been trained. Altogether, 80 per cent of the Egyptian Army's equipment in Sinai was lost. Some 500 tanks were destroyed and a further 300 captured, as well as 450 guns and 10,000 vehicles of different types, including APCs.

Against the Royal Jordanian Army, which employed British and American tanks and followed British tactical practice, the Israelis had a much tougher battle and on one occasion came close to defeat before they managed to clear the West Bank, but against the Syrians holding the Golan Heights they achieved another spectacular success, using troops rapidly re-deployed from Samaria and Sinai. The Syrians had also adopted a defence in depth with three infantry brigades manning the front and a further three forming a second line of defence at Mas'ada, Quneitra and Rafid, each

Another view of the raiding force showing three of the four T-55s involved *(Eshel Dramit Ltd)*.

of the six brigades being supported by a 30-strong T-34/SU-100 battalion. The counter-attack force consisted of one armoured brigade with 40 T-54s at Q'ala, a second with 90 T-54/55s at Quneitra and a third with 90 T-54/55s at Kfar Nafekh.

The Israeli assault began on 9 June and, although the Syrians fought extremely hard throughout the day, by mid-morning on the 10th they were becoming demoralised by air strikes and increasingly unsettled by moves directed against their flanks and rear. By noon they had commenced a disorderly withdrawal through Quneitra and that evening Damascus requested and was granted a ceasefire. The fighting on the Golan had cost the Syrian Army approximately 100 of its tanks.

Within the USSR the results of the Six Day

This photograph of an Israeli-manned T-55 illustrates graphically one of the principal defects of Soviet tank design, namely that the limited degree of depression available to the main armament inhibits the ability to fight hull-down *(Eshel Dramit Ltd)*.

On 9 September 1969 an Israeli amphibious raid on the Egyptian coast using captured T-55s and BTR-50P APCs produced spectacular results. The vehicle on the crest is one of the T-55s *(Eshel Dramit Ltd)*.

**After the Six Day War
the Israeli Army
converted a substantial
number of captured
T-55s to its own use by
replacing the 100 mm
gun with the British-
designed 105 mm** *(Eshel
Dramit Ltd)*.

War gave rise to grave concern, the obvious
implications being that there was something
seriously wrong with Soviet equipment and
methods. Faced with such a loss of prestige,
the Kremlin spared no expense to convince its
Arab clients that this was not the case, the lost
tanks, guns and aircraft being promptly replaced by more up-to-date equipment. For his
part, Nasser refused to accept that hostilities
had ended and embarked on what has subsequently become known as the War of Attrition, lasting from the autumn of 1967 until
July 1970. This took the form of artillery
exchanges, commando raids and air strikes
across the Suez Canal, which continued to
separate the Egyptian and Israeli armies.

One interesting episode involved an Israeli
amphibious raid on 9 September 1969, directed at the Egyptian coast of the Gulf of Suez,
the landing force consisting of four T-55s and
three BTR-152 APCs which had been captured in Sinai. The vehicles were still painted
in Egyptian colours and aroused little interest
until they opened fire. They were ashore for
eight hours before re-embarking, having destroyed radar installations at Ras Abu-Daraj
and Ras Za'afrana, raided camps and inflicted
several hundred casualties including a number
of senior officers and their Soviet advisers.
Nasser sustained a heart attack on learning of
the incident and died shortly after the two sides

agreed to a ceasefire the following year. Israel
emerged from the War of Attrition as the
tactical victor but was actually in an unfavourable position when it ended as her policy of
long-range bombing attacks into Egypt provoked the Soviet installation of an air-defence
belt, including SAMs, along the Canal.

Soviet confidence was itself somewhat restored by the Warsaw Pact's invasion of Czechoslovakia on 21 August 1968, putting an end to
the challenge offered to the Party's rule by
more liberal elements. As an administrative
and logistic exercise the invasion was impressive but there was no fighting as the Czech
government, recognising the fact of the
country's isolation within the Soviet bloc and
wishing to avoid the sort of bloodbath that had
taken place in Hungary the previous decade,
ordered its army not to offer resistance. The
Soviet troops had been told that they were
liberating the country from Western influence
and were visibly taken aback by the hostile
reception they received in Prague and elsewhere, a number of tanks being set ablaze or
damaged in isolated incidents.

During the guerrilla phase of the long war in
Vietnam the communist forces made little use
of armour, but starting in February 1968 they
began using light tanks, frequently reported as
PT-76s although they were sometimes
Chinese Type 63s, in attacks against isolated
camps. Occasionally these met with some success, as at Lang Vei, but elsewhere they ended
in failure. By 1971 the North Vietnamese
Army (NVA) was also using T-54s and
Chinese Type 59s and in February these were
encountered in strength when the South Vietnamese Army (ARVN) attempted to cut the
Ho Chi Minh Trail by a raid into Laos.

In March 1972 the NVA launched a conventional offensive against the South, spearheaded
by armour at several points. The NVA crews,
however, soon demonstrated their inexperience when confronted by American-trained
ARVN tank units, and also lost heavily to
infantry tank-hunter teams, TOW missiles
launched from UH-1B helicopters and US
ground-attack aircraft. Although it was able to
report the occasional local success, in the main
the experience of the communist armour was
disastrous and resulted in the loss of over 150
tanks and numerous other AFVs. An ARVN
counter-offensive recovered much of the
ground that had been lost and in January 1973
both sides agreed to a ceasefire.

(Right) **South Vietnamese troops inspect a Chinese Type 59 medium tank captured in 1972** (USAMHI).

Following the withdrawal of the last US units from Vietnam and the reduction of military aid to the South, the NVA commenced a fresh offensive in March 1975. The lessons of 1972 had been absorbed and this time tank attacks were carefully co-ordinated with infantry and artillery support. The ability of the ARVN to resist had been radically diminished because of ammunition, fuel and spares shortages and it also lacked the devastating US air support which it had enjoyed hitherto. In places some units fought to the last, but on 30 April the NVA's 203rd Armoured Regiment broke into Saigon and reached the presidential palace, bringing the war to a symbolic conclusion. Peace, however, did not return to Indo-China. Relations between Vietnam and Kampuchea (Cambodia) deteriorated to the extent that in December 1978 the former launched a full-scale invasion, toppling the infamous dictator Pol Pot. China, which had close links with Kampuchea, mounted a punitive strike into northern Viet-

Rear view of NVA Type 59 medium tank knocked out during the 1972 offensive (USAMHI).

(Left) **T-55s and BTR-152 in position outside the parliament building in Prague** (AP).

Pakistan Type 59s in their distinctive dark green and white camouflage.

nam but withdrew after several weeks' inconclusive fighting.

After their war of 1965, India and Pakistan turned respectively to the USSR and China for additional AFVs with which to supplement their stock of Western tanks, India receiving approximately 450 T-54/55s and a smaller number of PT-76s, while Pakistan was supplied with 50 T-54s, 225 Type 59s and some Type 63 light tanks. When war broke out again in 1971 the Indians emerged the victors from several armoured engagements in the Punjab but lost some ground on the Chaamb sector. A post-operational analysis suggested that the Indian T-54/55s' night-fighting aids had given them a technical advantage over Pakistan's Type 59s, which lacked such equipment, as did the possession of more recently developed ammunition. In East Pakistan the Indians employed T-55s and PT-76s, the latter proving of great value in crossing the country's numerous waterways, the only armoured opposition being provided by a single fragmented regiment equipped with M24 light tanks, which was quickly disposed of.

In the Middle East both Egypt and Syria, now fully equipped with modern Soviet AFVs, aircraft and missiles, were determined to avenge their defeat in the Six Day War and launched co-ordinated attacks on Israel at

14:00 hrs on 6 October 1973, coinciding with the celebration of Yom Kippur, the holiest day in the Jewish calendar, and thereby achieving complete surprise at every level and initiating a war which was to witness the largest tank battles since World War 2.

On the Golan the Israeli position was fronted by an anti-tank ditch but the line was thinly held by two armoured brigades with a total of 170 Centurions and M48 Pattons. Leading the Syrian attack were three infantry divisions, each with its own organic tank brigade, while the second echelon consisted of the 1st and 3rd Armoured Divisions; this gave the Syrians a total of 1,500 T-55s and T-62s, plus 1,000 guns ranged against the Israelis' 60 artillery pieces. An additional danger for the

During the 1971 Indo-Pakistani War the Indians avoided confusion between their own T-55s and Pakistan's Type 59s by fitting a dummy fume extractor to their gun barrels, which then resembled the British 105 mm from a distance.

In October 1973 this sector of the Golan front became known as The Valley of Tears. Wrecked MTU bridgelayers and other AFVs provide mute evidence of the Syrians' failure to cross the anti-tank ditch *(Eshel Dramit Ltd)*.

This T-62 has crabbed sideways into the anti-tank ditch, burying the muzzle of its gun *(Eshel Dramit Ltd)*.

Another view of The Valley of Tears showing a litter of knocked-out T-55s *(Eshel Dramit Ltd)*.

Syrian T-62, blown to
pieces during the
desperate fighting on
the Golan (Eshel Dramit
Ltd).

Israelis was that, like NATO, they had very little space to trade, for a Syrian breakthrough would mean the isolation of northern Galilee. Everything, therefore, hinged on holding the line until the reserve armoured formations could mobilise and reach the front.

The Syrian attack was pressed home with suicidal courage but the MTU bridgelayers were quickly knocked out and superior Israeli tank gunnery shot yawning gaps in the advancing ranks. The unequal battle raged all that afternoon and through the night until the following morning the defence on the southern sector was swamped and the Syrian 1st Armoured Division began to pour through the gap. The Israelis' desperate stand, however, had served its purpose, for throughout the evening of the 7th the leading elements of their reserve armoured formations had begun to enter the battle, halting the Syrian probes towards the Upper Jordan. During the next two days a major part of the 1st Armoured Division was encircled and ultimately destroyed at Hushniya, frantic attempts to break through to it by its remaining armoured brigade and part of 3rd Armoured Division being defeated. By nightfall on 10 October the Syrians had retired behind the old ceasefire line, having sustained in five days of ferocious fighting the loss of 867 tanks, hundreds of guns and APCs, thousands of assorted other vehicles and huge quantities of smashed or abandoned equipment.

The following day the Israelis capitalised on

their victory by advancing into Syria to a point from which Damascus could be brought under long-range artillery fire, maintaining their positions on hostile territory despite daily counter-attacks by the remains of the Syrian Army, the Soviet-equipped Iraqi 3rd Armoured Division, the Jordanian 40th Armoured Brigade and a small Moroccan contingent. By the time a ceasefire was mutually accepted on 22 October, Syrian tank losses had soared to 1,150, the Iraqis losing a further 200 and the Jordanians 50. Israeli tank losses during the campaign amounted to 250, of which 150 were repairable.

On the Suez Front both the Soviet Army's concept of surprise and its techniques for crossing water obstacles were fully vindicated on 6 October, although the crossing itself was made in the face of negligible opposition. On the southern sector the crossing was made by the Egyptian Third Army with two infantry divisions, each reinforced with an armoured brigade, followed in due course by the 4th Armoured and 6th Mechanised Divisions. In the centre the 130th Marine Brigade effected a crossing of the Great Bitter Lake using PT-76 light tanks and BTR-50P APCs. On the northern sector the crossing of the Egyptian Second Army was made with three infantry divisions, each of which was again supplemented by an armoured brigade, followed by the 21st Armoured and 23rd Mechanised Divisions.

The strongpoints of the Bar Lev Line— actually a chain of fortified observation posts—

fell without undue difficulty in the majority of cases, and local counter-attacks made by the one Israeli regular armoured division in Sinai were easily contained by a combination of ATGWs, tank and artillery fire so that by the evening of the 7th no less than 170 Israeli tanks had been destroyed or put out of action. The Egyptians dug in and awaited the major counter-offensive which they knew would follow the arrival of their opponents' reserve formations at the front.

This began at 08:00 hrs on 8 October and was based on the faulty premise that the Egyptians were breaking out of their bridgeheads. The axis of the attack was from north to south, i.e. parallel to the Egyptian positions, but by mid-morning the Israelis realised their mistake and swung hard right to engage the enemy head-on, meeting a defence that was even stronger than it had been the previous day. The rest of the day was spent in a fruitless battle of attrition in which the Israelis were worsted, the armoured division most concerned (Adan's) losing 70 of its tanks, of which 20 were recovered after dusk.

The failure deeply depressed the Israelis, who were forced to remain on the defensive while the enemy's build-up continued. The scale of the Egyptian crossing had come as a tremendous shock, as had the massed use of ATGWs, but the latter were countered by placing more mechanised infantry and artillery at the disposal of commanders of armoured divisions, restoring the tactical balance which

had been absent since the Six Day War, and as the war progressed it became clear that the appearance of the ATGW did not signal the demise of the tank, as some sections of the media hastily predicted. The use of ATGWs in this manner was, in fact, an intelligent expedient resorted to by the Egyptians, who did not believe that they would be able to get as many of their tanks into the bridgeheads in the first day of the war as was actually the case, and they were aware that such a measure was unlikely to achieve surprise again.

The Egyptians were also aware that they were no match for their opponents in a fast-moving battle of manoeuvre and the objectives they set for their planned offensive were strictly limited, including the Mitla, Giddi and Tassa Passes and the logistic complex at Bir Gifgafa, without which they felt that the Israelis would be unable to support themselves in Sinai. Moreover, they were not inclined to attack before their air defence cordon had been moved forward to cover their operations. However, the situation in Syria demanded that the Egyptian Army should take positive action to assist its stricken ally and on 14 October some 800 tanks pushed out towards the Israeli defences along the Sinai Front. These were engaged in a day-long gunnery duel against the Israeli armoured divisions and by evening had been forced to withdraw into their positions, leaving 250 of their number burning on the battlefield. A major factor in the Egyptian defeat was the limited depression available on their tanks' main armament, which inhibited them from taking full advantage of hull-down fighting positions; an Israeli armoured brigade, equipped with captured T-55s re-armed with the British 105 mm gun, was similarly handicapped and sustained serious loss.

Events now began to move at a pace at which the Egyptian high command was unable to respond. The Israelis had already detected a gap between the Second and Third Armies and during the night of 15/16 October effected a crossing of the Canal despite intense efforts to seal off the penetration. During the 17th the Egyptian 25th Armoured Brigade, equipped with T-62s, ran into a tank ambush and was destroyed as it attempted to enter the battle by driving north along the eastern shore of the Great Bitter Lake. On the west bank of the Canal the Israeli armour systematically eliminated SAM sites as it drove south to encircle the Third Army, which was pounded to scrap by air attack and was in danger of dying of thirst when a ceasefire finally took effect on 24 October.

The results of the October 1973 Arab–Israeli War could hardly be viewed with satisfaction by the Kremlin, the most important consequences of which were Egypt's conclusion of a peace treaty with Israel and her withdrawal from the Soviet sphere of influence. Syria, on the other hand, remained even more dependent on Soviet aid and her losses were more than made good with the most modern equipment available.

Events in Africa soon began to claim the Soviets' attention. In 1975 Portugal granted independence to her former colonies and in Angola fighting broke out betwen pro- and anti-Marxist guerrilla factions. The Marxist MPLA, on the brink of losing what amounted to a civil war, appealed for aid and in November the first contingent of Cuban troops arrived, bringing with them 90 T-34/85s and T-54s and several batteries of 122 mm rocket launchers. The introduction of heavy weapons soon tilted the balance in the MPLA's favour, enabling it to defeat the rival FNLA in the north and then confine the South African-backed UNITA forces to the south-east of the country, following which it was recognised as the *de facto* government of the country. UNITA, however, remains a force to be reckoned with and continues to inflict reverses on joint Cuban/government forces, which have

also sustained casualties and loss of vehicles and equipment in local clashes with the South African Army during the latter's cross-border anti-terrorist strikes.

In the Horn of Africa the Soviet Union found herself in something of a dilemma, for two of her clients, Ethiopia and Somalia, were contesting possession of the Ogaden region. By June 1977 the Somalis had pushed the ramshackle Eritrean army out of the Ogaden and were positioned on the Ahmar Mountains, besieging Harar. Thus far, the Soviets had attempted to be even-handed in the dispute but when the Somalis expelled them in November they decided to give Ethiopia their full support and commenced the shipment of heavy weapons by sea and air. These included several hundred T-54/55s, BMP and BMD IFVs, ASU-57 airborne assault guns, 122 mm and 152 mm howitzers, multi-barrel rocket-launchers, jet aircraft and helicopters. So seriously did the Kremlin regard the affair that General Vasili Petrov, then First Deputy Commander of Soviet Ground Forces, was detailed to plan and co-ordinate the Ethiopian counter-offensive, which was to be spearheaded by 11,000 Cuban troops. The Cuban contingent, which included a parachute regiment, were unfamiliar with the BMP and BMD but were quickly trained in their use.

The offensive opened on 6 February 1978, taking the form of a frontal assault in the mountains combined with a left hook around the northern end of the Ahmar massif. The Somalis, demoralised by constant air strikes and sustained rocket-launcher fire, were forced to abandon their siege of Harar but retired to prepared positions at the Kara Marda Pass and Jigjiga, where artillery and a T-55 battalion were dug in, and throughout the remainder of the month resisted all attempts to eject them.

At the northern end of the front, however, the local Somali units had been defeated by a series of parachute and air-landing operations involving twenty Mil-8 and ten Mil-6 helicopters flown by Soviet pilots. Petrov decided to use this asset against the garrison of Jigjiga and on 5 March a similar operation secured a landing zone at Genasene, 28 km (17 miles) north of the town. Into this were lifted 70 ASU-57 assault guns which drove south and attacked the defences from the rear while they were simultaneously under pressure from a frontal assault. Resistance collapsed with heavy loss of life and on 8 March Somalia

announced her intention of withdrawing from
the Ogaden.

In December 1979 the Soviet Union gave
further proof of its air-landing capability during its invasion of Afghanistan, some details of
which have been given elsewhere. To achieve
surprise, the motor rifle divisions which were
involved in the invasion employed recalled
reservists from Turkestan and Uzbekistan.
This proved to be a mistake, for most of these
men were Muslims and generally sympathetic
to Afghan aims, provoking such a crisis of
morale that many units have had to be replaced
with others drawn from the Central Reserve.

In general, the experience of the Soviet
Army in Afghanistan has been an unhappy
one. Trained almost exclusively for a conventional mechanised offensive, it has had to learn
the techniques of counter-insurgency and
mountain warfare, and the evidence suggests
that the process has been painful. Beyond the
boundaries of the cities and their own fortified
bases, the Soviets' writ counts for little, despite

punitive area bombing which has depopulated
large areas of the country. Furthermore, the
Afghan Army, which the Soviets are nominally
present to support, has proved a broken reed,
being so plagued by desertion as to provide a
regular supply of weapons for the Mujahedin
guerrillas.

Of necessity, movement between bases has
had to be confined to heavily escorted convoys
which are, nonetheless, subject to constant
attack by an enemy whom centuries of tribal
warfare have made expert in the art of ambush.
Tanks proved to be quite unsuited to work of
this type and most were withdrawn, being
replaced by additional APOs and IFVs which
could provide the sustained firepower required
as well as an infantry response.

As the war progressed the Soviets initiated
an air-mobile version of the technique once
employed by British troops on the North-West
Frontier of India. Before a column moves
along a valley troops are lifted by helicopter on
to the heights on either side, and once the

column has passed they are similarly extracted and re-inserted on hills further down the valley; if the Mujahedin attempt to interfere, they are engaged by prowling gunships. This has reduced the toll in casualties, wrecked AFVs and other vehicles, but it has brought the end of the conflict no nearer. It is a matter of concern to the Soviet Army that it is apparently unable to impose a decision after so long and there are signs that the Kremlin would gladly be quit of its involvement could an acceptable solution be found.

Another unresolved conflict is the long and bloody Gulf War between Iraq and Iran, which began in 1980. Iraq is believed to have entered the war with over 2,000 MBTs, the majority being T-54/55s and T-62s, plus a hundred or so T-72s. These equipped four armoured divisions, two mechanised divisions and an independent mechanised brigade. The Iranians possessed approximately 875 Chieftains, 400 M48 Pattons and 460 M60A1s, equipping the equivalent of three armoured divisions and an independent armoured brigade. The pattern the war has followed consists of periodic local offensives by one side or the other, which are first contained and then driven back by a counter-offensive. Despite the bitter and self-sacrificial nature of the fighting neither army seems to possess the ability to inflict a major defeat on its opponent. Heavy loss of life has been accompanied by wholesale destruction of equipment, to the extent that today each side is at least partially equipped with a proportion of the other's tanks that have been salvaged from the battlefield.

In the troubled state of Lebanon the struggle for power between the Christians, Muslims and the Palestine Liberation Organisation (PLO) erupted into civil war in 1975. The following year an Arab Deterrent Force, of which the Syrian 3rd Armoured Division formed the major element, crossed the frontier to police the country, fighting several sharp actions against the PLO. This restored peace for a while but in February 1977 fighting broke out again in the south and continued intermittently until 1981. Because of Israeli support for the Christians the Syrians felt compelled to take sides with the local Muslim militias and the PLO.

For many years Israel had been subjected to PLO terrorist attacks originating in southern Lebanon and on 6 June 1982 she launched a major cross-border strike under the codename of Operation PEACE FOR GALILEE, the objects of which were to break the PLO's power in Lebanon and eliminate the Syrian presence in the Beka'a Valley. During this operation the Israelis deployed their new Merkava tank for the first time. Between 7 and 10 June heavy fighting took place around Jezzin and in the Beka'a Valley, held by the Syrian 1st Armoured Division, equipped with T-62s and T-72s. The Syrians made good use of ground to inflict loss but were pushed steadily back, losing 72 of their tanks. The Israelis were initially a little worried by the presence of the T-72, which they had not encountered before, and the destruction of several drew the laconic comment from Major-General Yanush Ben Gal, commanding the Israeli armour on this sector, that 'they burn just like any other tank'. Ultimately, the Israelis managed to cut Syrian communications with Beirut, where what were the remnants of the PLO continued to be besieged until agreeing to evacuate the city at the end of August.

ANNEX: ORGANISATIONAL TABLES

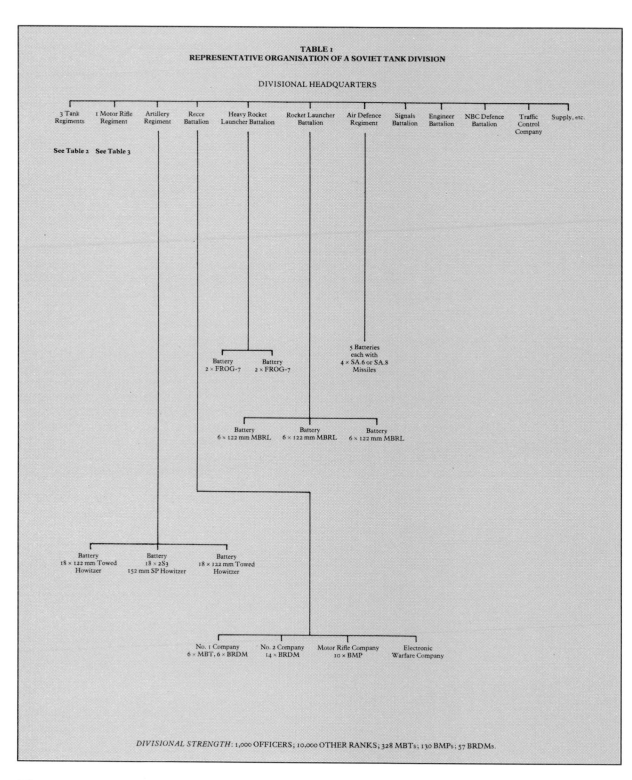

TABLE 1
REPRESENTATIVE ORGANISATION OF A SOVIET TANK DIVISION

DIVISIONAL HEADQUARTERS

| 3 Tank Regiments | 1 Motor Rifle Regiment | Artillery Regiment | Recce Battalion | Heavy Rocket Launcher Battalion | Rocket Launcher Battalion | Air Defence Regiment | Signals Battalion | Engineer Battalion | NBC Defence Battalion | Traffic Control Company | Supply, etc. |

See Table 2   **See Table 3**

Battery 2 × FROG-7   Battery 2 × FROG-7

5 Batteries each with 4 × SA.6 or SA.8 Missiles

Battery 6 × 122 mm MBRL   Battery 6 × 122 mm MBRL   Battery 6 × 122 mm MBRL

Battery 18 × 122 mm Towed Howitzer   Battery 18 × 2S3 152 mm SP Howitzer   Battery 18 × 122 mm Towed Howitzer

No. 1 Company 6 × MBT, 6 × BRDM   No. 2 Company 14 × BRDM   Motor Rifle Company 10 × BMP   Electronic Warfare Company

DIVISIONAL STRENGTH: 1,000 OFFICERS; 10,000 OTHER RANKS; 328 MBTs; 130 BMPs; 57 BRDMs.

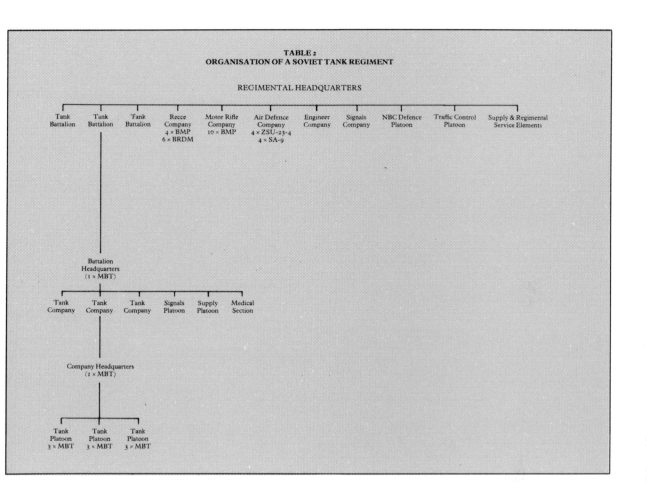

TABLE 2
ORGANISATION OF A SOVIET TANK REGIMENT

REGIMENTAL HEADQUARTERS

| Tank Battalion | Tank Battalion | Tank Battalion | Recce Company 4 × BMP 6 × BRDM | Motor Rifle Company 10 × BMP | Air Defence Company 4 × ZSU-23-4 4 × SA-9 | Engineer Company | Signals Company | NBC Defence Platoon | Traffic Control Platoon | Supply & Regimental Service Elements |

Battalion Headquarters
(1 × MBT)

| Tank Company | Tank Company | Tank Company | Signals Platoon | Supply Platoon | Medical Section |

Company Headquarters
(1 × MBT)

| Tank Platoon 3 × MBT | Tank Platoon 3 × MBT | Tank Platoon 3 × MBT |

153

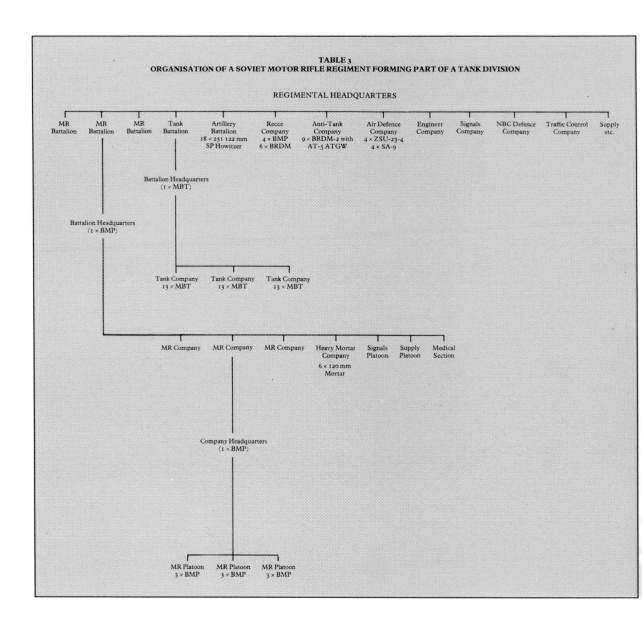

TABLE 3
ORGANISATION OF A SOVIET MOTOR RIFLE REGIMENT FORMING PART OF A TANK DIVISION

REGIMENTAL HEADQUARTERS

| MR Battalion | MR Battalion | MR Battalion | Tank Battalion | Artillery Battalion 18 × 251 122 mm SP Howitzer | Recce Company 4 × BMP 6 × BRDM | Anti-Tank Company 9 × BRDM-2 with AT-5 ATGW | Air Defence Company 4 × ZSU-23-4 4 × SA-9 | Engineer Company | Signals Company | NBC Defence Company | Traffic Control Company | Supply etc. |

Battalion Headquarters
(1 × MBT)

Battalion Headquarters
(1 × BMP)

| Tank Company 13 × MBT | Tank Company 13 × MBT | Tank Company 13 × MBT |

| MR Company | MR Company | MR Company | Heavy Mortar Company 6 × 120 mm Mortar | Signals Platoon | Supply Platoon | Medical Section |

Company Headquarters
(1 × BMP)

| MR Platoon 3 × BMP | MR Platoon 3 × BMP | MR Platoon 3 × BMP |

154

TABLE 4
REPRESENTATIVE ORGANISATION OF A SOVIET MOTOR RIFLE DIVISION

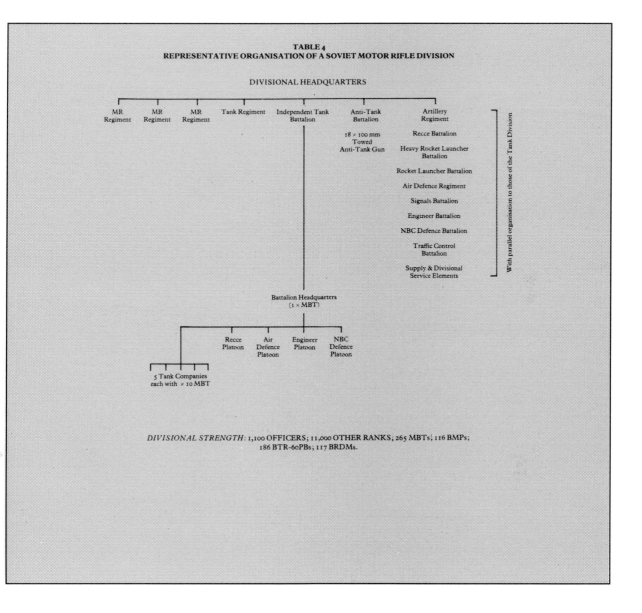

DIVISIONAL STRENGTH: 1,100 OFFICERS; 11,000 OTHER RANKS; 265 MBTs; 116 BMPs; 186 BTR-60PBs; 117 BRDMs.

155

TABLE 5
ORGANISATION OF SOVIET MOTOR RIFLE REGIMENTS EQUIPPED WITH BTR-60PB APCs
FORMING PART OF A MOTOR RIFLE DIVISION

REGIMENTAL HEADQUARTERS

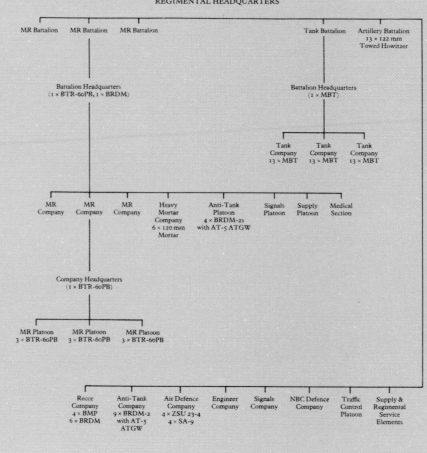

156

SELECT BIBLIOGRAPHY

Bonds, Ray, Ed., *Modern Tanks and Fighting Vehicles*, Salamander.

Bonds, Ray, Ed., *The Soviet War Machine*, Salamander.

Dinter, Elmar and Griffith, Paddy, *Not Over By Christmas*, Antony Bird.

Foss, C. F., Ed., *Jane's Armour and Artillery*, Jane's.

Isby, David C., *Weapons and Tactics of the Soviet Army*, Jane's.

Lee, Christopher, *The Last Decade*, Hamish Hamilton.

Magnuski, Janusz, *Wozy Bojowe*, Wydawnictwo Ministerstwa Obrony Narodowej, Warsaw.

Messenger, Charles, *Anti-Armour Warfare*, Ian Allan.

Perrett, Bryan, *A History of Blitzkrieg*, Robert Hale.

Perrett, Bryan, *Knights of the Black Cross*, Robert Hale.

Sándor, Dr Mucs and Magda, Fábri, *Bákeörségben*, Zrinyi Katonai Kiadó, Budapest.

v. Senger und Etterlin, Dr F. M., *Taschenbuch der Panzer*, J. F. Lehmanns Verlag, Munich.

Simpkin, Richard, *Mechanized Infantry*, Brassey's Defence Publishers.

Simpkin, Richard, *Red Armour*, Brassey's Defence Publishers.

Suvarov, Viktor, *Inside the Soviet Army*, Hamish Hamilton.

Vigor, P. H., *Soviet Blitzkrieg Theory*, Macmillan.

Weeks, Colonel John, *Armies of the World*, Jane's.

Zaloga, Steven J., *Soviet Tanks Today*, Arms and Armour Press.

GLOSSARY

AGS	*Automatichesky Granatomat Stankovy*—automatic grenade launcher.
ASU	*Aviadesantnaya Samochodnaya Ustanovka*— airborne self-propelled mounting.
BAV	*Bol'shoi Plavaiuschii Avtomobil*—large amphibious truck.
BMD	*Bronevaya Maschina Desantnaya*—airborne combat vehicle.
BMP	*Bronevaya Maschina Piekhota*—armoured infantry vehicle.
BRDM	*Bronevaya Rasvedyvateinya Dosornaya Maschina*—armoured reconnaissance vehicle.
BTR	*Bronetransportr*—armoured personnel carrier.
GSP	*Gusenichnii Samochodni Parom*—tracked self-propelled ferry.
IMR	*Inzhenarnaia Maschina Ragzazhdenaia*— engineer obstacle-clearing vehicle.
MTU	*Mostovoi Transportr Ustanovka*—bridge transporter mounting.
OT	*Obrneny Transporter*—armoured transport vehicle.
PMP	*Pontonna Mostovoi Park*—pontoon bridging train.
PT	*Plavuchii Tank*—amphibious tank.
SKOT	*Sredni Kolowy Opancerzny Tranporty*—heavy armoured personnel carrier.
SU	*Samochodnaya Ustanovka*—self-propelled mounting.
TMM	*Tiazhelyi Mekhanizirovanny Most*— heavy truck-mounted bridge.
ZSU	*Zenitnaya Samochodnaya Ustanovka*—self-propelled anti-aircraft mounting.

INDEX

Numbers in *italic* refer to illustration captions